First Steps

Developing Literacy Skills

for 5 - 6 year olds

Compiled by
D C Perkins, BA (Hons), MEd, PhD (Wales) and E J Perkins, BSc (Hons), MEd

Design and Illustration Anthony James
Educational Adviser Alison John, BEd

DOMINO BOOKS (WALES) LTD
SWANSEA SA1 1FN
Tel. 01792 459378 Fax. 01792 466337
First Steps, Developing Literacy Skills for 5 - 6 year olds © EJP and DCP 1999.
ISBN 1 85772 152 7

Contents

Page

How To Use This Book   3

ACTIVITY SHEETS/SUBJECTS

Subjects are listed at the bottom of each activity sheet

CONTENTS TEACHERS' NOTES See next page

Contents

Teachers' Notes

Name _____

Alphabet flowers

Read and say the words on the leaves then write them on the correct petals.

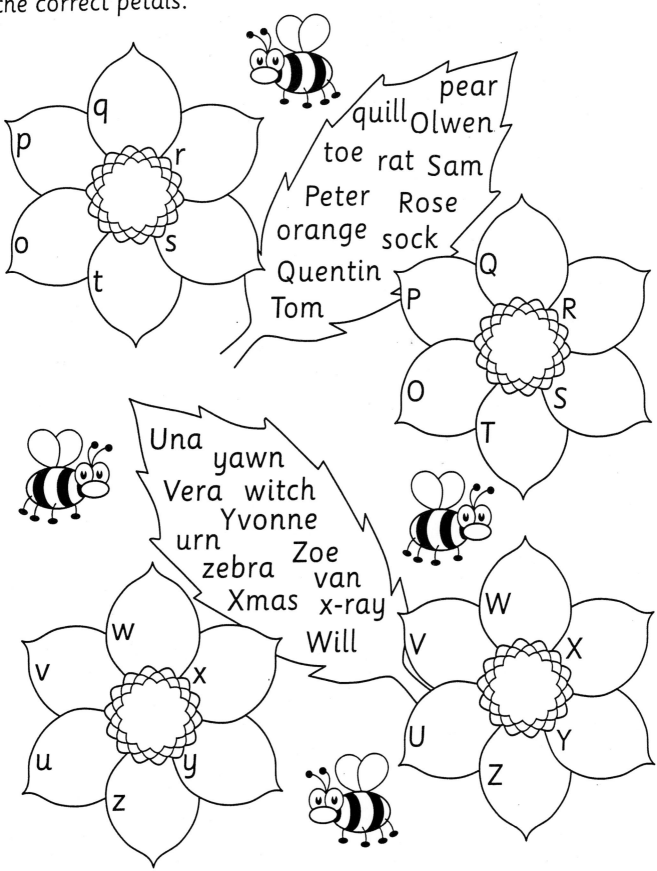

Developing Literacy Skills 5-6 Years © EJP and DCP

Name _____

These are the lockers where the football team keep their kit.

The members of the team are
Fred, Pam, Ann, Ron, Jill, Tim, Sam, Bill, May, Dan, Len.

Write their names on the alphabet ladder.
Next write their names on the lockers in alphabetical order.

Alphabet ladder:
- A
- B
- C
- D
- E
- Fred
- G
- H
- I
- J
- K
- L
- M
- N
- O
- P
- Q
- R
- S
- T
- U
- V
- W
- X
- Y
- Z

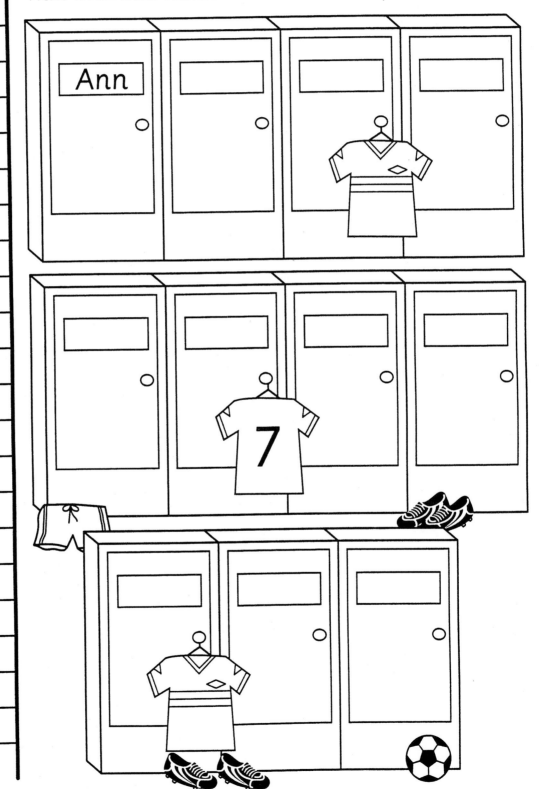

Ann

7

Name _____

Say the words. Write at or an to finish the words.

b____   v____   h____   m____

r____   c____   c____   p____

_____

List four words that end with at or an.

at	an

Write the missing words.

The c____ chases the r____ .

The m____ drives the v____ .

Name _____

Say the words. Write ad or ap to finish these words.

l____   n____   t____   m____

c____   d____   s____   p____

List four words that end with ad or ap.

ad	ap

Write the missing words.

The boy wearing a c____
looks at the m____.

The l____ lost his d____
and is s____ .

Name _____

Say the words. Write in or ip to finish the words.

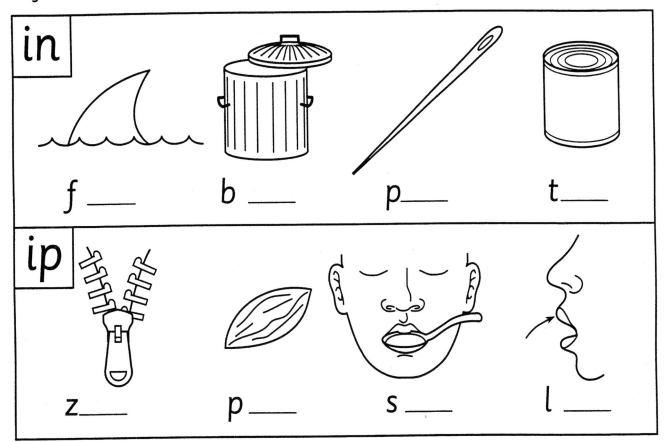

in

f ___   b ___   p___   t___

ip

z___   p ___   s___   l ___

Colour blue the words that rhyme with fin.
Colour yellow the words that rhyme with zip.

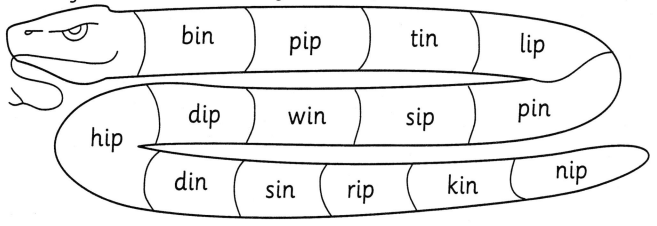

bin   pip   tin   lip

hip   dip   win   sip   pin

din   sin   rip   kin   nip

Find the missing words.

Jane used a p___to fasten her coat.

There was a p___in the orange.

Jack closed the z___of the case.

Paul wanted to w___the race.

This means a tear in material. r___

Anne took a small s___of tea.

Sam opened the t___of beans.

Emma put all the rubbish in the b___.

Len wanted to try the lucky d___.

A fish uses this to swim. f___

Name _____

Say the words. Write ig or it to finish the words.

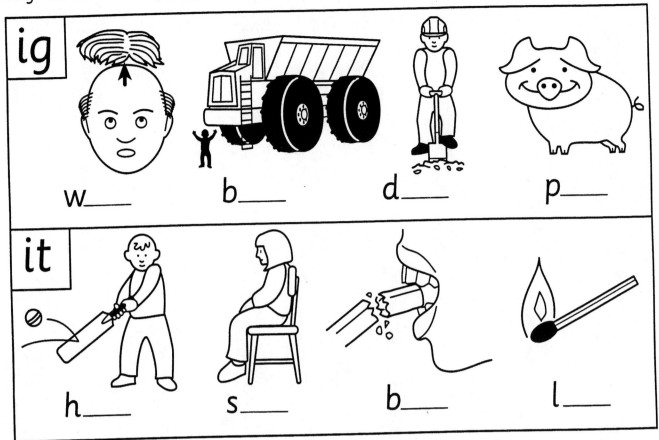

ig

w____   b____   d____   p____

it

h____   s____   b____   l____

Colour brown the words that rhyme with big.
Colour green the words that rhyme with sit.

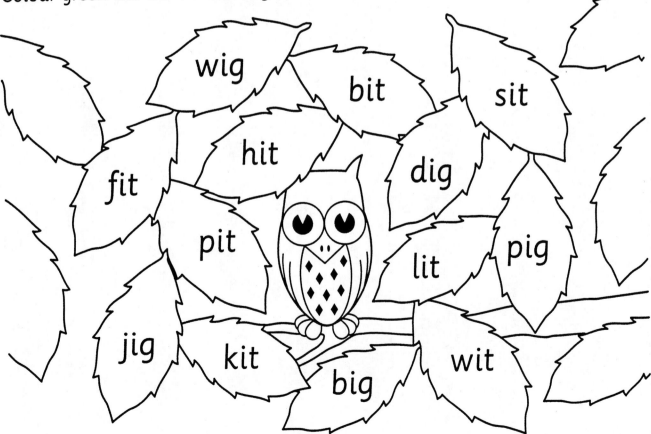

Name _____

Wordsearch

Colour ten words that have ch, sh or th in them.

c	h	a	i	r	f	i	s	h
r	c	h	i	p	s	l	y	z
s	h	i	p	b	c	h	i	n
b	o	s	h	e	e	p	l	j
t	e	e	t	h	m	n	q	f
m	o	t	h	s	h	e	l	l
n	n	c	h	u	r	c	h	d

Match the words you have found to the pictures.

_____   _____   _____

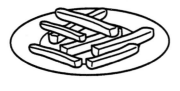

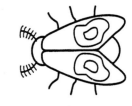

_____   _____   _____   _____

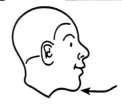

_____   _____   _____

Name _____

Say the words. Write bl, cl or fl to finish these words.

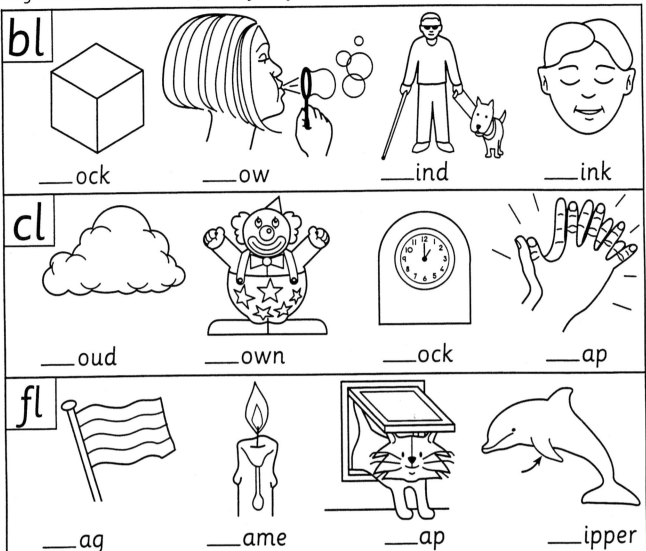

bl			
__ock	__ow	__ind	__ink

cl			
__oud	__own	__ock	__ap

fl			
__ag	__ame	__ap	__ipper

Finish the words.

1. Samantha can bl____bubbles.

2. The cl____made the children laugh.

3. The candle fl____burned brightly.

4. The girl waved the fl____.

5. The children cl_____their hands.

1.

3.

2.

5.

4.

Name _____

Say the words. Write sp, sl or sn to finish the words.

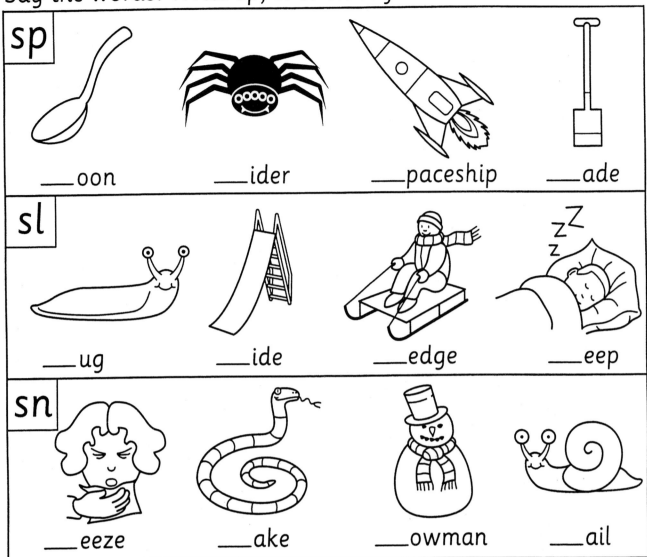

sp

___oon   ___ider   ___paceship   ___ade

sl

___ug   ___ide   ___edge   ___eep

sn

___eeze   ___ake   ___owman   ___ail

Use the words you have made to solve these puzzles.

Has 8 legs and makes a web.

_____

You make this with snow.

_____

Astronauts travel in this.

_____

Hisses when disturbed.

_____

You use this to eat soup.

_____

Has its 'house' on its back.

_____

You dig holes with this.

_____

Slides on ice and snow.

_____

You do this when you are tired.

_____

Slimy and lives in the garden.

_____

Name _____

Sort these words into lists.

wall	pill	fall	tell
call	will	mill	yell	ball
bell	still	well	hill

Sort these words into sets with the same ending.

-all	-ell	-ill

Write the words under the pictures.

_____   _____   _____

_____   _____   _____

Name _____

Words and Numbers

Draw lines to match the words and numbers.

_____

Find the missing numbers.

Developing Literacy Skills 5-6 Years © EJP and DCP

Name _____

Words and Numbers

Draw lines to match the words and numbers.

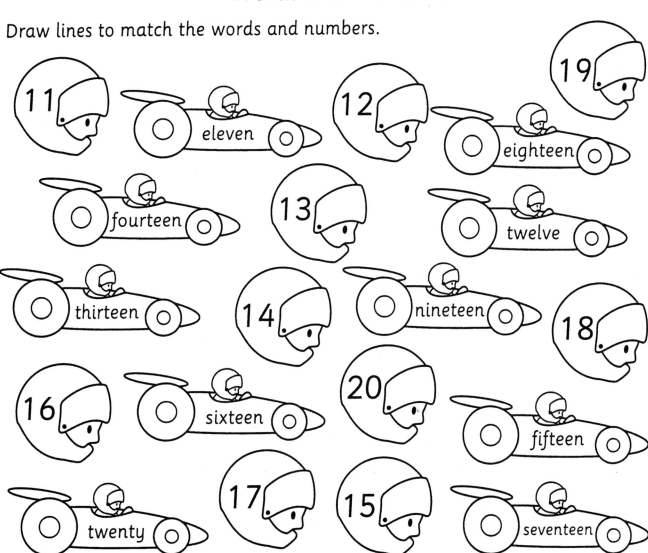

Find the missing numbers.

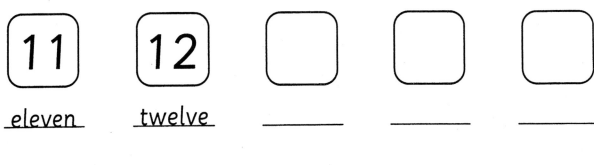

eleven   twelve   _____   _____   _____

_____   _____   _____   _____   twenty

Name _____

Making Sense

Circle the correct word to finish each sentence.

 The elephant is   small   big.

Patch is   sad   happy.

 The cat is   sleeping   awake.

The bird is   swimming   flying.

 The man is   tall   short.

The cat is   dry   wet.

 Ice cream is   hot   cold.

John is   last   first.

 The ball is   square   round.

Name _____

Capital letters and full stops

Circle the capital letters at the beginning of these sentences and the full stops at the end.

I like ice-cream.

The dog is barking.

There are cakes for tea.

John won the race.

Write the capital letters and full stops in these sentences.

☐T☐ the sun is shining ☐.☐

☐ ☐ ladybirds have spots ☐

☐ ☐ give the ball to Sam ☐

☐ ☐ tidy the bookshelf ☐

☐ ☐ we are playing cricket ☐

☐ ☐ i am riding my bike ☐

Name _____

Nouns

A
Look at the picture. Find 10 things and list them below.

B
The names of things in the picture.

_____

_____

_____

_____

_____

_____

_____

_____

_____

_____

C
Look at the picture and finish these sentences.

1. The _____ is on the wall.

2. The girl is riding a _____ .

3. The boy is kicking a _____ .

4. The _____ is shining.

5. The _____ is flying.

6. The _____ is barking at the _____ .

Name _____

More Nouns

Write five different things or nouns under each heading.

in school
_____
_____
_____
_____
_____

at home
_____
_____
_____
_____
_____

clothes
_____
_____
_____
_____
_____

toys
_____
_____
_____
_____
_____

pets
_____
_____
_____
_____
_____

wild animals
_____
_____
_____
_____
_____

vegetables
_____
_____
_____
_____
_____

favourite foods
_____
_____
_____
_____
_____

Here are a few suggestions:
desk, cupboard, television, bed, coat, shoes, teddy, football,
cat, dog, lion, tiger, carrot, potatoes, crisps, beef burger.

Name _____

What are they doing?

Write a caption under each drawing.
Choose from:

swimming

drawing

climbing

drinking

skipping

Name _____

? ? ? ? Question Marks ? ? ? ?

A Put a question mark at the end of each sentence.

1. What are you doing

2. Is this your book

3. What is your name

4. Why is the baby crying

5. When does the match start

6. Who is ringing the doorbell

7. Which seat would you like

8. Where did you put your hat

9. Who wants the last cake

10. Can you jump

B Put a full stop or a question mark at the end of each sentence.

1. Is it time to go to school

2. It is early

3. Where shall we go

4. We are going to the cinema

5. I like ice-cream

6. Do you like cakes

? ? ? ? ? ? ? ? ? ? ? ?

Name _____

Addresses

Bill is having a birthday party and these are the invitations to his friends.

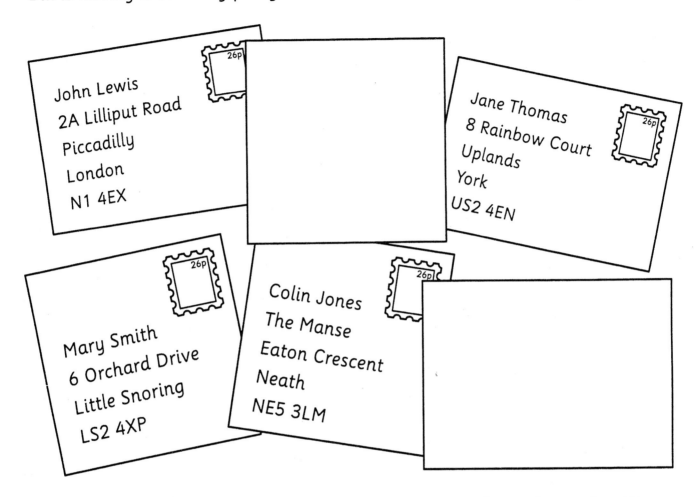

1. Who lives in London?_____

2. Who lives in Little Snoring?_____

3. Who lives at the Manse?_____

4. Who lives at 8 Rainbow Court?_____

5. Helen James lives at

   7 West Avenue

   Townhill

   Reading

   RY3 4LM

   Address the invitation to Helen.

6. Address one to yourself.

   Remember to draw the stamps.

Make a list of Bill's guests. Remember to include yourself.

Name _____

The Queen of Hearts

Read the nursery rhyme about the Queen of Hearts and look at the pictures.

Cut out the pictures and put them in the correct order.

Paste the correct caption from the nursery rhyme under each picture.

Colour the pictures.

The Queen of Hearts
She made some tarts
All on a summer's day:

The Knave of Hearts
He stole those tarts,
And took them clean away.

The King of Hearts
Called for the tarts,
And Beat the Knave full sore:

The Knave of Hearts
Brought back the tarts,
And vowed he'd steal no more.

Name _____

The Queen of Hearts
The Next Day

Pretend you are a journalist on the local paper, The Heartfordshire Gazette. Write an account of what happened at the Palace.

only 25p

The Heartfordshire Gazette

Knave of Hearts steals tarts

_____
_____
_____

_____   _____
_____   _____
_____   _____
_____   _____
_____   _____

Name _____

Learning to Swim

These pictures are about Jan learning to swim.

Cut out the pictures and put them in the correct order to make a story.

Paste in the correct captions and colour the pictures.

Choose from these captions.

> Jan likes swimming with her mother.
>
> Jan and her mother arrive at the sports centre.
>
> Jan puts on her arm bands.

Name _____

Sequencing

Write the letters to show which picture comes first.
One has been done for you.

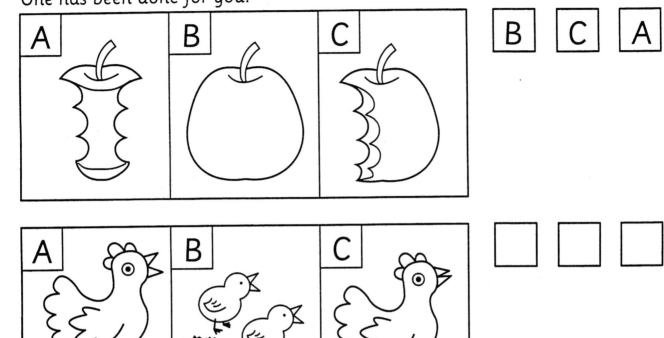

| B | C | A |

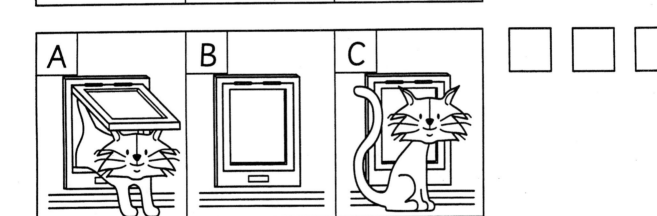

| | | |

| | | |

| | | |

Draw three pictures to show the beginning, middle and end of something you do.

Name _____

Stories

Write these stories beginning:

1. One day, Emma and Jane went for a walk in the woods with their dog, Rags. Suddenly, they heard the dog barking ...

2. Jack had been watching a film about a ghost who was lost. When it finished he switched off the television and went to sleep.
   Next morning, when he woke up, there sitting on the bottom of his bed was ...

3. Tim and his sister carefully put the hat on the snowman they had just built. They turned away to go back to the house.
   'Just a minute,' said a voice behind them ...

4. Sammy the squirrel was worried. He could not find where he had hidden his nuts for the winter ...

5. I waved the magic twig ...

Write these stories ending:

1. Jemma felt opening a present would never be the same.

2. The dragon promised he would never frighten anyone again.

3. I stepped out of the space ship. It had been exciting but I was glad to be home.

4. Jimmy smiled at the clown and the clown smiled back. At last the clown was happy once more.

5. William listened to the shouts of the crowd. It has been the happiest day of his life.

The National Literacy Strategy
Sight Words
Flash Cards

I	at	are
up	for	this
look	he	going
we	is	they
like	said	away
and	go	play
on	you	a

took	old	once
made	next	out
make	much	our
many	night	over
may	not	people
more	how	school
name	now	take
new	off	than

their	time	when
them	very	where
then	were	who
there	what	your
these		Thursday
Monday		Friday
Tuesday		Saturday
Wednesday		Sunday

All these words, except 'that' are also in the 20 words most often used in writing.

The following words make up a further 10% of all words read:

as, at, but, had, him, his, not, on, all, be, are, for, have, one, said, so, they, we, you

Most of these words are also in the 50 words most often used in writing.

SHORT VOWEL SOUNDS

When the children are confident with single initial letter sounds and shapes, it is time to tackle the short vowel sounds in small (three-letter) words with the CVC (consonant-vowel-consonant) pattern. They learn to recognise the sounds and to understand the changes made in sound and meaning that occur when the vowel is changed, e.g. hat/hit/hot/hut. Rhyming words help children become familiar with similar sounds and predict the sounds of groups of letters.

CONSONANT BLENDS AND END CLUSTERS

Children should become aware of some of the more commonly used blends, e.g. bl-, cl-, fl-, gl-, pl-, sl-, br-, cr-, dr-, fr-, gr, tr-, st- and -st, sp-, sl-, sn-, -all, -ell, -ill, -iss, -oss, -oll, -ck, -ff, -lf and -ng.

MAKING NEW WORDS

Children need to understand that it is possible to build new words from knowledge they have already gained. Rhyme helps in the recognition of similar endings.

NUMBERS, DAYS AND MONTHS

Children are aware of number and need to know the words and symbols. They should know the days of the week and the months of the year. This information is usually first acquired through their interest in birthdays.

SENTENCE LEVEL

Very young children communicate successfully using body language and single words. Often, only their mother can understand them. By the age of 5 they have acquired a small but useful vocabulary and have started to string words together to make sense. They also enjoy making silly sentences which are amusing. Learning to make sense of spoken or written language is sometimes a struggle for adults. We understand the individual words but not the meaning of the utterance and sometimes miss the hidden message. Pictures help children discover different interpretations and help them to make sense of the information they are given.

SENTENCES

Children need to recognise the sentence as a unit of language, that it is complete and makes sense. They need to understand that a sentence
1. ends with a full stop.
2. begins with a capital letter.

Children need practice in making up sentences beginning with very simple ones consisting of just a subject and a verb. They have to learn to write a full stop at the end and to begin each sentence with a capital letter. They should be able to tell if a string of words is a sentence or not, if it makes sense or does not.

NOUNS

Children usually have no difficulty in naming things. They should know that the names of people and places have capital letters. As they learn the names of days and months, they will also learn that they begin with capital letters

VERBS

Asking children what they are doing or like doing or playing leads to the understanding of verbs and how a verb differs from a noun.

QUESTION MARKS

A question mark can be introduced as a special kind of full stop used when you want to know something, that is, to ask a question.

Children need to be able to decide whether to use a full stop or a question mark at the end of a sentence.

MAKING SENSE

Using language, children learn that there is an accepted sequence of words that makes sense. This skill is acquired as children learn to talk but it can be developed by simple activities and exercises. Too much attention may cause confusion.

STYLE AND FORMAT

Children need to be aware that there is an accepted way of writing addresses, invitations … This is usually introduced when they make greeting cards and invitations.

STORIES AND READING

READING ACTIVITIES

Reading is one of the most important skills acquired by children. We read for information and very importantly, for pleasure. Reading should be presented as something to be enjoyed.

'Reading' pictures. This leads to an understanding that drawings, pictures, that is material on a page, has meaning. Children begin to identify this material with their surroundings and what happens to them. Realising that a flat drawing represents a soft, fat, cuddly toy is a remarkable achievement. [Most of us have been driven to distraction constructing the simplest object using diagrams in an instruction sheet!]

CAPTIONS

This is one of the simplest forms of reading and children quickly learn to match names and familiar objects. Later, the concept is developed using action pictures or a sequence of events in a story or rhyme.

SIGNS

It is important that children learn to read information on signs such as BOOK CORNER, NATURE TABLE, STOP, NO ENTRY and so on.

SITUATION PICTURES

These. e.g 'in the park', can be discussed and children should be able to suggest what is happening and tell about their own experiences.

Where necessary prompt with, for example, 'What/who is that? What are they doing?' 'Where are they?' and when appropriate, 'What do you think will happen next?'

SEQUENCING AND MATCHING

These skills are important as a basis for the recognition of groups of letters and words. Begin with simple pictures and ask what will happen next. Drawings of familiar stories and nursery rhymes shown first in sequence and then out of order are useful.

TELLING STORIES.

Children like to be told stories. This widens their experiences and imagination beyond their own surroundings. They should be encouraged to tell stories themselves. They may tell a story from the view of one or more of the characters in the story or as a reporter/newsreader/investigator.This develops vocabulary, imagination and memory.

Drawing This helps children understand and relate to material on the page as well as developing motor skills. Always encourage children to colour their work. Ask them to tell you what their picture is about.

Predicting. Saying what will happen next helps children think about the picture in front of them and develops imagination.

MATCHING.

Finding out what is the same or different between two or more pictures develops observational skills. Reading depends on instant recognition of letters and groups of letters that are the same or different. Comparing pictures of the same place at different times introduces the concept of change and why changes occur.

Focusing on detail. Reading depends on detailed recognition. Paying attention to details around them, in pictures and in books helps to develop these skills. When learning to write, children are helped to learn the shapes of letters by copying them. Exercises in letter recognition - those that are the same and the 'odd letter out' are helpful.

Children use a variety of clues and skills to read. Pictures are very important and if the story is familiar, there may well be some intelligent guessing. It is important to encourage the children to make progress and not become lost in a sea of print. Encourage children to sit comfortably and to sit upright.

METHODS USED TO TEACH READING

Phonic method. This aims to build up an understanding of how our alphabet works, of the letters and the sounds they represent. It enables children to say words they do not know.

Look and say. This aims to teach children a growing sight vocabulary of complete words that they can recognise and say at once. It relies on repetition and requires a scheme with a controlled vocabulary.

'Real' books/whole language. This approach aims to absorb children's attention by using exciting stories and natural language so the children begin to focus on, predict and remember the words they see. The stories selected do not necessarily come from a particular reading scheme.

HOW A BOOK WORKS.

Children need to know
how to hold a book.
how the cover of a book is different from the inside.
that we keep the book still and turn the pages. (Encourage the children to turn the pages when you read).
that the pictures are full of interesting information.
that a story is exciting to listen to.

Shared reading involves groups of children reading large books with enlarged text. Children may be asked to identify key words in the text, to find words beginning with a particular letter or containing particular letters and simple cloze tests in which a word is covered and the children make an informed guess.

READING CORNER

When children start to take an interest in books or other reading material, it is important that there is a quiet place where they can look at books or read in peace. This may be a favourite chair or in nursery it may be a corner with chairs, stools, several large cushions, a desk and a mat.

EARLY WRITING SKILLS

PRE-WRITING SKILLS

Sequencing and matching are important as a basis for writing later on. For example, adding tails to animals, colouring and tracing activities, cutting and pasting are part of the early development of these important skills. Teach the children to hold crayons and pencils 'properly'.

Scribbling. A child's first efforts look like random marks on a surface. Encourage the use of pens, pencils and crayons. Avoid 'disasters' by ensuring that the children learn where they can work and have comfortable surroundings. This is play and should be enjoyed.

Tracking. Children should be taught to track vertically and horizontally.

Letter development. Letters emerge from the scribbling. Often, children use just one letter to represent a word. Show that in English, writing starts at the top left hand corner of a page and proceeds from left to right and down the page. Children will see writing all around them. When they are read to, they begin to realise that written words have meaning. They soon have favourite stories that they want read again and again.

Copying. Children are helped to learn the shapes of letters by copying them. This may be by writing over the top of existing letters or copying. Show the children how to form letters correctly.

Independent writing. When children begin to remember words and spelling develops, they start to write simple sentences or phrases.

Some children are more comfortable using their left hand. In general, allow a child to use which hand he/she prefers.

WORD LEVEL ACTIVITIES

These provide a link between the reading of whole texts and the teaching of letter-sound relationships.

1. **Games and recitations** of rhyming, alliterative and onomatopoeic songs, stories and poems
2. **I spy.** Adapt games in which children say as many words as they can remember with the same beginnings or endings.
3. **Odd one out.** This involves recognising a word that differs from the others in a series.
4. **Alphabet frieze.** Let the children make a large alphabet frieze.
5. **Use alphabets** of names, animals and so on.
6. **Make vocabulary lists.**

HANDWRITING

Children should examine the differences and similarities between letters. They should track letters and trace dot-to-dot patterns. Tracing letters in sand or in the air is also helpful.

ENCOURAGING WRITING AND COPYING

Encourage children to contribute to different activities.

1. **Family words.** Make large cards for the children and their families so that the names are special for them.
2. **Museum corner and labels.** Children should bring items that are special to them. The objects are then labelled and displayed. This can have a changing theme every week.
3. **Special occasion cards.** Children can design and write cards, e.g. for birthdays, invitations,Christmas and

Page 25 On the Farm
farmer, cat, scarecrow,
hen, cows, dog,
sheep, duck, pig

Page 26 ch, sh, th
chin, chair, chips, church
fish, ship, shell, sheep
teeth, thimble, three, moth

shop, fish, chips
bench, finch
path

Page 27 Wordsearch

```
c h a i r f i s h
r c h i p s l y z
s h i p b e h i n
b o s h e e p l j
t e e t h m n q f
m o t h s h e l l
n n e h u r c h d
```

church, shell, chair
fish, chips, teeth, moth
sheep, ship, chin

Page 28 bl-, cl-, fl-
block, blow, blind, blink
cloud, clown, clock, clap
flag, flame, flap, flipper

blow, clown, flame, flag, clapped

Page 29 pl-, gl-, sl-
plug, plum, plane, planet
glove, glass, glue, igloo
slug, slide, sledge, sleep

plum	slug
plane	glue
glove	sledge
glass	sleep

Page 30 br-, cr-, dr-

brush	crab	drain
bread	crown	drip
bride	cracker	drum
brick	crisps	drink

drink, brush, crown, crab
wed, cracker, drain, crisps
drum, bread, brick, drip

Page 31 fr-, gr-, tr-
frog, fry, frown, frame
grapes, grin, grass, gran
train, tree, tractor, trolley

fry	tractor
grass	frog
train	grapes
frame	frown
trolley	grin

Page 32 st
string, star, stool, stamp
fist, first, burst, crust.

st-	-st
string	fist
star	first
stool	burst
stamp	crust

star, fist, first, stamp

Page 33 sp-, sl-, sn-
spoon, spider, spaceship, spade
slug, slide, sledge, sleep
sneeze, snake, snowman, snail

spider	snail
snowman	spade
spaceship	sledge
snake	sleep
spoon	slug

Page 34 -all   -ell   -ill

wall	tell	pill
fall	yell	will
call	bell	mill
ball	well	hill

bell, well, hill
mill, ball, wall

Page 35 -iss, -oll, -oss
Red: hiss, kiss, miss
Yellow: moss, toss, cross, boss
Green: doll, roll

iss	oss	oll
hiss	moss	doll
kiss	toss	roll
miss	cross	
	boss	

doll, kiss, hiss
cross, roll, toss

Page 36 Rhyming Words

bat	ran	nap	mad
rat	van	tap	dad
mat	man	map	pad
ten	wet	bed	peg
men	net	wed	leg
pen	vet	fed	beg
tin	pip	wig	bit
bin	zip	big	hit
fin	lip	fig	sit
dog	hot	top	nod
cog	dot	cop	cod
log	pot	mop	rod
cut	jug	sun	mud
hut	hug	bun	bud
nut	mug	run	dud

Page 37 Make New Words

dam	yet
ham	set
jam	get
ram	let
fan	son
ran	ton
tan	won
man	Ron
sit	fog
hit	hog
fit	dog
lit	log
sum	den
mum	Ben
gum	pen
hum	hen
box	fix
fox	six
cox	mix

Page 38 Make New Words

duck	ring
truck	king
sock	sing
lock	spring

duck, sock, ring, song
truck, lock, king, spring

Page 39 Words and Numbers
one/1, two/2, three/3, four/4, five/5,
six/6, seven/7, eight/8, nine/9, ten/10
2,   4,   6,   7,   9
two, four, six, seven, nine

Page 40 Words and Numbers
eleven/11, twelve/12, thirtee/13
fourteen/14, fifteen/15, sixteen/16,
seventeen/17, eighteen/18,
nineteen/19, twenty/20

13,   14,   15,   16,
thirteen, fourteen, fifteen, sixteen,
   17,   18,   19
seventeen, eighteen, nineteen

Page 41 More Than One
dogs, cats, bees, ants, frogs

Singular	Plural
cat	cats
bat	bats
hen	hens
owl	owls
dog	dogs
rat	rats
ant	ants
frog	frogs
bird	birds

Page 42
In the Park

Toilets   Shop

No fishing   Duck Pond

   Picnic Area   Play Area

No Bikes   Park

Page 43 Alice Goes Shopping
Biscuits
Cola

Page 46 Making Sense
big, happy, sleeping, flying, tall, wet,
cold, first, round

Page 48 Beginnings and Endings
1. Jane is riding her bike.
2. John is playing football.
3. The hen has laid an egg.
4. Kofi is skating on the ice.
5. We get milk from cows.
6. Ann is painting a picture.
7. The ducks swim in the pond.
8. The girl's name is Amy.
9. Sam is flying his kite.
10. A spider spins a web.

Page 49 Missing Words
1. honey   2. eat   3. flew
4. blue, black 5. Leaves   6. sea
7. Hens,   8. rained   9. red
10. fingers, toes

Page 51 Nouns
dog, cat, wall, boy, girl, ball, bike, sun,
tree, bird ...
1. cat   2. bike   3. ball
4. sun   5. bird   6. dog, cat

Page 55 At the Zoo
Names of people
and things (red)   Doing words (green)
Bill   walked
Mary   quacked
zoo   swam
ducks   jumped
lake   climbed
monkey   ate
tree   roared
giraffe   bought
leaves
lion
ice-creams
shop

Page 56   I
1. Jim likes
   I like computer games
2. Helen has
   I have two brothers.
3. Kate is
   I am eating an apple.
4. Sam is
   I am making a snowman.
5. Mary is
   I am going to the shops.
6. John is
   I am playing football.
7. Tony
   I can tell the time.
8. Jack is
   I am drinking a glass of milk.
9. Jill is   her
   I am putting my shoes on.
10. Mum is   her
   I am riding my bike.

Page 57 John's Diary
B 1. John went swimming and
     sorted his books.
  2. On Tuesday.
  3. On Wednesday
  4. A new football.
  5. Star Wars. On Friday.
  6. On Sunday
C Monday:
  I played a new computer game.
  Tuesday:
  I went to a theme park with my
  brother. We had to be home by 7.30.
  Saturday morning:
  I went shopping with my mother.
  Sunday morning:
  I helped my brother clean his motor
  bike.

Page 58 Questions Marks
B Questions marks at the end of 1, 3, 6
  Full stops at the end of 2, 4, 5

Page 59 Addresses
1. John Lewis
2. Mary Smith
3. Colin Jones
4. Jane Thomas

  John Lewis
  Helen James
  Jane Thomas
  Mary Smith
  Colin Jones
  Me

Page 61 The Birthday Party
apples, bread, crisps, ham, ice-cream
jelly, lemonade, milk, oranges,
sausages

Page 62 Mum's Calendar
March, April, May, June, July,
August, September, October,
November
A   1. 1. January at 11.30.
    2. 12 February
    3. School holiday ends
    4. 31 October
    5. 21 December

Page 63 Sentence Practice 1
A   1. blue   2. hopped
    3. Sunday   4. tractor   5. cold

B   1. The cat drinks the milk.
    2. The door bell rang loudly.
    3. The sheep had a woolly coat.
    4. The dog had a sore paw.
    5. The baby sleeps in the pram.

Page 64 Sentence Practice 2
A man, fish, bird, dog, boy, ice-cream,
   tree, flowers, frog, pond

B 1. The man is fishing.
   2. The fish are swimming.
   3. The bird is flying.
   4. The dog is sleeping.
   5. The boy is eating ice-cream.

Page 70 Pictures and Captions
Fishing   Baby sleeping   Feeding
                in his pram   the ducks

Reading   Skateboarding   Eating an
                                ice-cream

Swimming   Tennis   Football

Page 73 Sequencing
CAB
BAC

Page 74 Make a Teddy Bear
1. Cut out the pieces from the teddy
   bear fabric.
2. Sew the pieces together.
3. Fill the teddy bear with cotton wool.
4. When you have finished use a pen to
draw his nose, eyes and mouth.

Page 75 Making Biscuits
1. First weigh the flour, sugar and
   butter.
2. Rub the flour and butter together
   and stir in the sugar. Add a beaten
   egg to make the dough.
3. Roll out the dough and cut out the
   biscuits.
4. Bake in a hot oven.

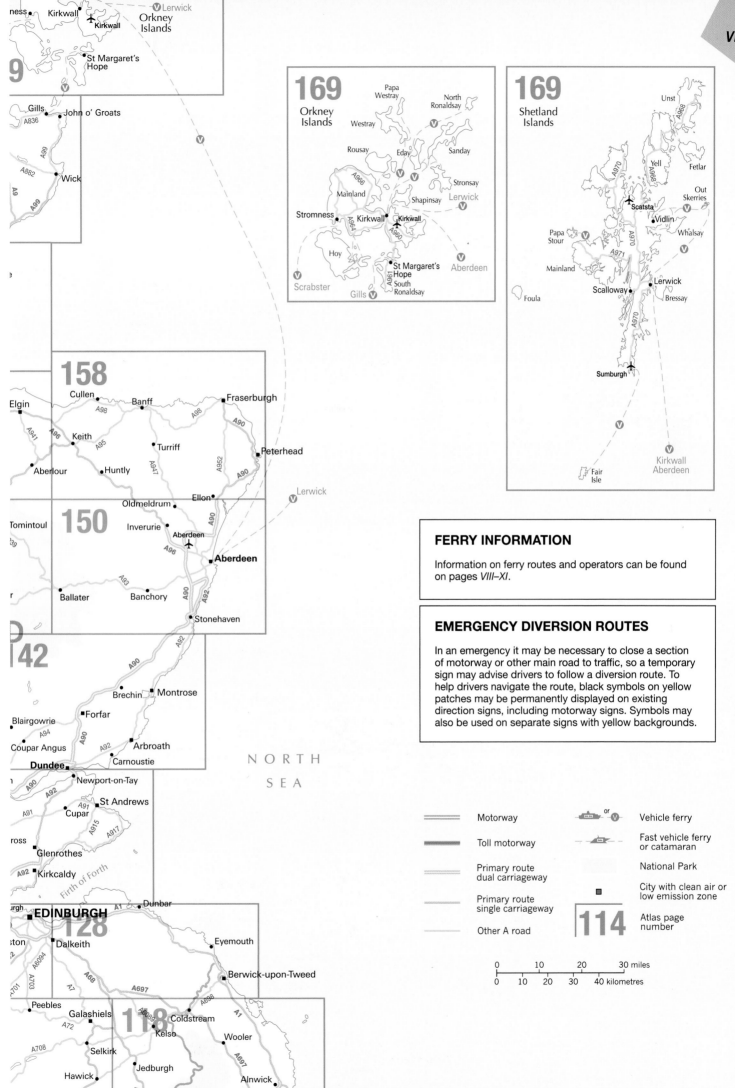

FERRY INFORMATION

Information on ferry routes and operators can be found on pages *VIII–XI*.

EMERGENCY DIVERSION ROUTES

In an emergency it may be necessary to close a section of motorway or other main road to traffic, so a temporary sign may advise drivers to follow a diversion route. To help drivers navigate the route, black symbols on yellow patches may be permanently displayed on existing direction signs, including motorway signs. Symbols may also be used on separate signs with yellow backgrounds.

Motorway

Toll motorway

Primary route dual carriageway

Primary route single carriageway

Other A road

Vehicle ferry

Fast vehicle ferry or catamaran

National Park

City with clean air or low emission zone

114 Atlas page number

0   10   20   30 miles
0   10   20   30   40 kilometres

Channel hopping and the Isle of Wight

For business or pleasure, hopping on a ferry across to France, the Channel Islands or Isle of Wight has never been easier.

The vehicle ferry services listed in the table give you all the options, together with detailed port plans to help you navigate to and from the ferry terminals. Simply choose your preferred route, not forgetting the fast sailings (see ⛴). Bon voyage!

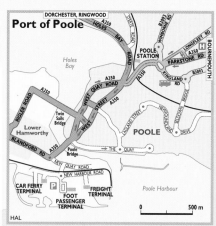

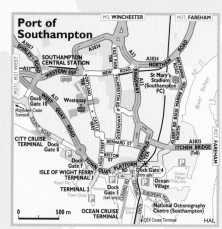

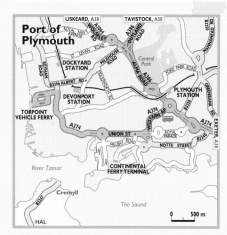

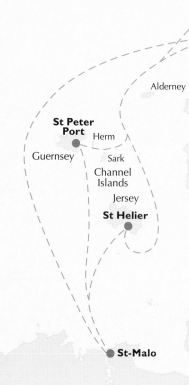

ENGLISH

Plymouth

Roscoff

St-Malo

St Peter Port

Herm

Guernsey

Sark

Channel Islands

Jersey

St Helier

Alderney

ENGLISH CHANNEL AND ISLE OF WIGHT FERRY CROSSINGS

From	To	Journey time	Operator website
Dover	Calais	1 hr 30 mins	dfdsseaways.co.uk
Dover	Calais	1 hr 30 mins	poferries.com
Dover	Dunkirk	2 hrs	dfdsseaways.co.uk
Folkestone	Calais (Coquelles)	35 mins	eurotunnel.com
Lymington	Yarmouth (IOW)	40 mins	wightlink.co.uk
Newhaven	Dieppe	4 hrs	dfdsseaways.co.uk
Plymouth	Roscoff	5 hrs 30 mins	brittany-ferries.co.uk
Poole	Cherbourg	4 hrs 30 mins (Apr–Oct)	brittany-ferries.co.uk
Poole	Guernsey	3 hrs ⛴	condorferries.co.uk
Poole	Jersey	4 hrs ⛴	condorferries.co.uk
Poole	St-Malo	6 hrs 20 mins–12 hrs (via Channel Is.) ⛴	condorferries.co.uk
Portsmouth	Caen (Ouistreham)	5 hrs 45 mins–7 hrs	brittany-ferries.co.uk
Portsmouth	Cherbourg	8 hrs	brittany-ferries.co.uk
Portsmouth	Fishbourne (IOW)	45 mins	wightlink.co.uk
Portsmouth	Guernsey	7 hrs	condorferries.co.uk
Portsmouth	Jersey	8–11 hrs	condorferries.co.uk
Portsmouth	St-Malo	11 hrs	brittany-ferries.co.uk
Southampton	East Cowes (IOW)	1 hr	redfunnel.co.uk

The information listed is provided as a guide only, as services are liable to change at short notice and are weather dependent. Services shown are for vehicle ferries only, operated by conventional ferry unless indicated as a fast ferry service (⛴). Please check sailings before planning your journey.

Travelling further afield? For ferry services to Northern Spain see brittany-ferries.co.uk.

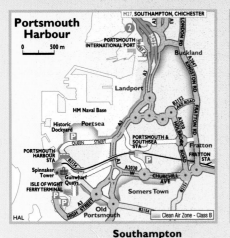

Portsmouth Harbour

Newhaven Harbour

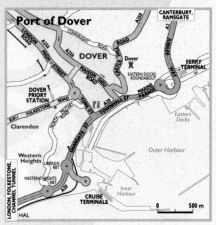

Port of Dover

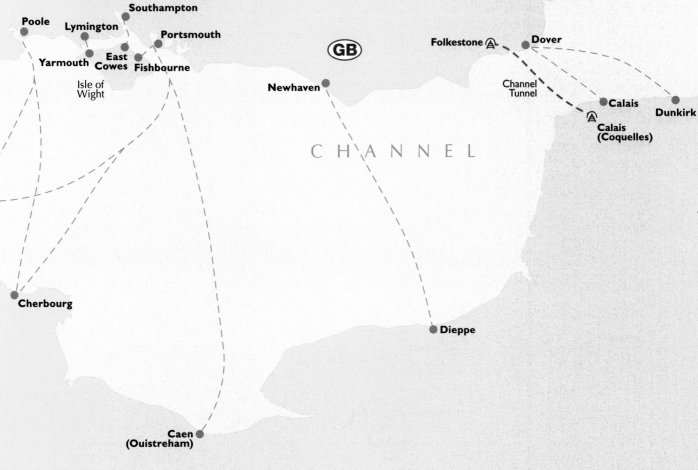

GB

Poole
Lymington
Southampton
Portsmouth
Yarmouth
East Cowes
Fishbourne

Isle of Wight

Newhaven

Folkestone

Dover

Channel Tunnel

Calais

Dunkirk

Calais (Coquelles)

C H A N N E L

Cherbourg

Dieppe

Caen (Ouistreham)

F

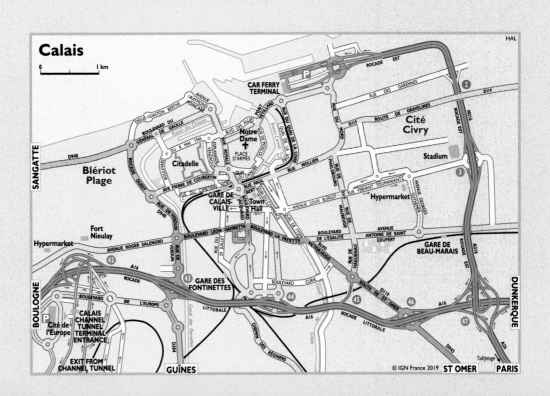

Calais

Refer also to atlas pages 58–59

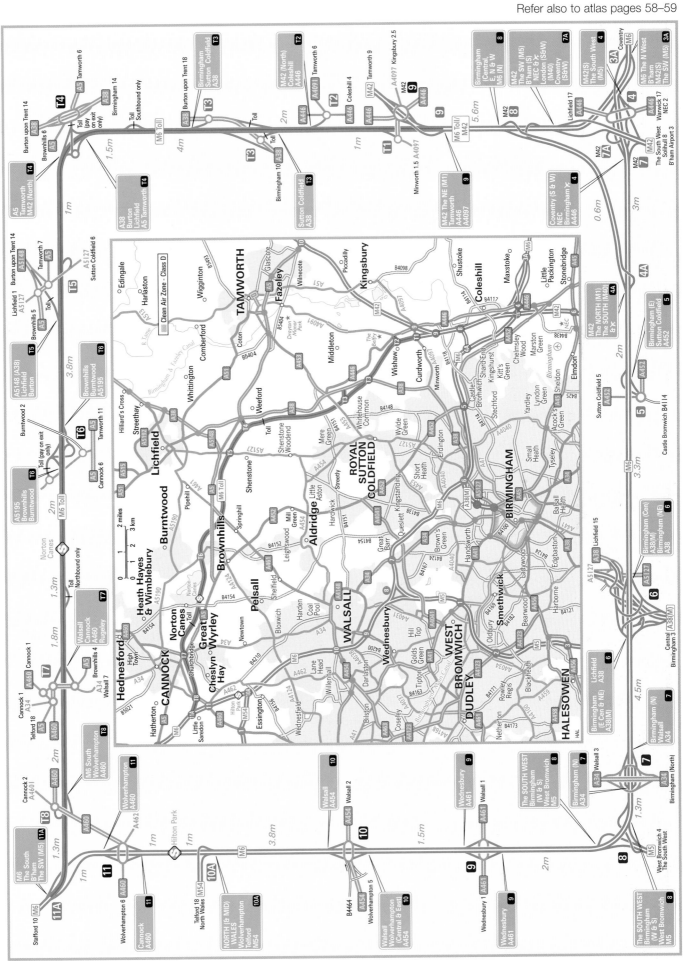

Smart motorways

Since Britain's first motorway (the Preston Bypass) opened in 1958, motorways have changed significantly. A vast increase in car journeys over the last 62 years has meant that motorways quickly filled to capacity. To combat this, the recent development of **smart motorways** uses technology to monitor and actively manage traffic flow and congestion.

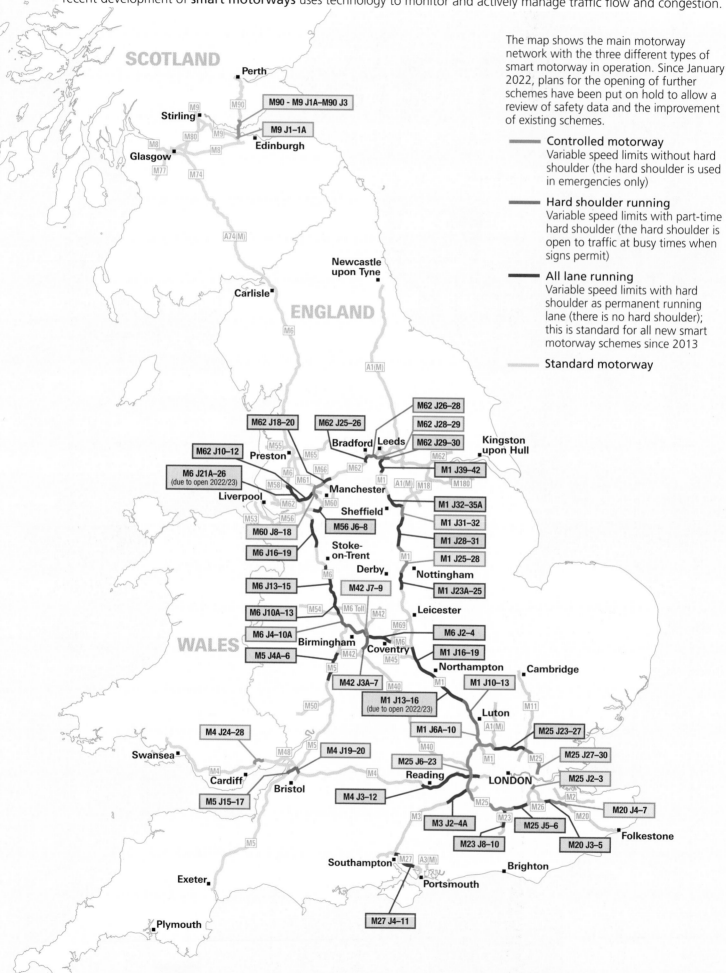

The map shows the main motorway network with the three different types of smart motorway in operation. Since January 2022, plans for the opening of further schemes have been put on hold to allow a review of safety data and the improvement of existing schemes.

Controlled motorway
Variable speed limits without hard shoulder (the hard shoulder is used in emergencies only)

Hard shoulder running
Variable speed limits with part-time hard shoulder (the hard shoulder is open to traffic at busy times when signs permit)

All lane running
Variable speed limits with hard shoulder as permanent running lane (there is no hard shoulder); this is standard for all new smart motorway schemes since 2013

Standard motorway

SCOTLAND

Perth

M90 - M9 J1A–M90 J3

Stirling

M9 J1–1A

Edinburgh

Glasgow

Newcastle upon Tyne

Carlisle

ENGLAND

M62 J26–28
M62 J28–29
M62 J29–30
Kingston upon Hull

M62 J18–20
M62 J25–26
Bradford Leeds

M62 J10–12
Preston
M1 J39–42

M6 J21A–26
(due to open 2022/23)
Liverpool
Manchester

M1 J32–35A
M1 J31–32
Sheffield
M1 J28–31

M60 J8–18
M56 J6–8
Stoke-on-Trent
M1 J25–28

M6 J16–19
Derby
M6 J13–15
Nottingham
M1 J23A–25

M6 J10A–13
M42 J7–9
Leicester

M6 J4–10A
M6 J2–4
WALES
M5 J4A–6
Birmingham Coventry
M1 J16–19

Northampton Cambridge
M42 J3A–7
M1 J10–13
M1 J13–16
(due to open 2022/23)
Luton

M4 J24–28
M1 J6A–10
M25 J23–27

Swansea
M4 J19–20
M25 J27–30
Cardiff
M25 J6–23
Reading LONDON
M25 J2–3

Bristol
M4 J3–12
M20 J4–7

M5 J15–17
M3 J2–4A
M25 J5–6
Folkestone

M23 J8–10
M20 J3–5

Southampton
Exeter
Brighton

Portsmouth

Plymouth

M27 J4–11

Smart motorways (*Intelligent Transport Systems* in Scotland) are the responsibility of National Highways, Transport Scotland and Transport for Wales

How they work

Smart motorways utilise various active traffic management methods, monitored through a regional traffic control centre:

- Traffic flow is monitored using CCTV
- Speed limits are changed to smooth traffic flow and reduce stop-start driving
- Capacity of the motorway can be increased by either temporarily or permanently opening the hard shoulder to traffic

- Warning signs and messages alert drivers to hazards and traffic jams ahead
- Lanes can be closed in the case of an accident or emergency by displaying a red X sign
- Emergency refuge areas are located regularly along the motorway where there is no hard shoulder available

In an emergency

On a smart motorway there is often no hard shoulder so in an emergency you will need to make your way to the nearest **emergency refuge area** or motorway service area.

Emergency refuge areas are lay-bys marked with blue signs featuring an orange SOS telephone symbol. The telephone connects to the regional control centre and pinpoints your location. The control centre will advise you on what to do, send help and assist you in returning to the motorway.

If you are unable to reach an emergency refuge area or hard shoulder (if there is one) move as close to the nearside (left hand) boundary or verge as you can.

If it is not possible to get out of your vehicle safely, or there is no other place of relative safety to wait, stay in your vehicle with your seat-belt on and dial 999 if you have a mobile phone. If you don't have a phone, sit tight and wait to be rescued. Once the regional traffic control centre is aware of your situation, via the police or CCTV, they will use the smart motorway technology to set overhead signs and close the lane to keep traffic away from you. They will also send a traffic officer or the police to help you.

Refuge areas for emergency use only

Sign indicating presence of emergency refuge areas ahead

Emergency refuge area SOS

This sign is located at each emergency refuge area

Signs

Motorway signals and messages advise of abnormal traffic conditions ahead and may indicate speed limits. They may apply to individual lanes when mounted overhead or, when located on the central reservation or at the side of the motorway, to the whole carriageway.

Where traffic is allowed to use the hard shoulder as a traffic lane, each lane will have overhead signals and signs. A red cross (with no signals) displayed above the hard shoulder indicates when it is closed. When the hard shoulder is in use as a traffic lane the red cross will change to a speed limit. Should it be necessary to close any lane, a red cross with red lamps flashing in vertical pairs will be shown above that lane. Prior to this, the signal will show an arrow directing traffic into the adjacent lane.

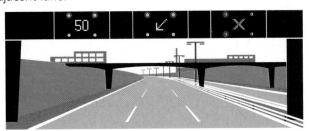

These signals are mounted above the carriageway with a signal for each traffic lane; each signal has two pairs of lamps that flash. You should obey the signal for your lane

Move to adjacent lane (arrow may point downwards to the right)

Leave motorway at next exit

Red lamps flashing from side to side in pairs, together with a red cross, mean 'do not proceed in the traffic lane directly below'. More than one lane may be closed to traffic

Where variable speed limit signs are mounted over individual lanes and the speed limit is shown in a red ring, the limit is mandatory. You will be at risk of a driving offence if you do not keep to the speed limit. Speed limits that do not include the red ring are the maximum speeds advised for the prevailing conditions.

Speed limits of 60, 50 and 40mph are used on all types of smart motorways. When no speed limit is shown the national speed limit of 70mph is in place (this is reduced to 60mph for particular vehicles such as heavy or articulated goods vehicles and vehicles towing caravans or trailers).

Quick tips

- Never drive in a lane closed by a red X
- Keep to the speed limit shown on the gantries
- A solid white line indicates the hard shoulder – do not drive in it unless directed or in the case of an emergency
- A broken white line indicates a normal running lane

- Exit the smart motorway where possible if your vehicle is in difficulty. In an emergency, move onto the hard shoulder where there is one, or the nearest emergency refuge area
- Put on your hazard lights if you break down

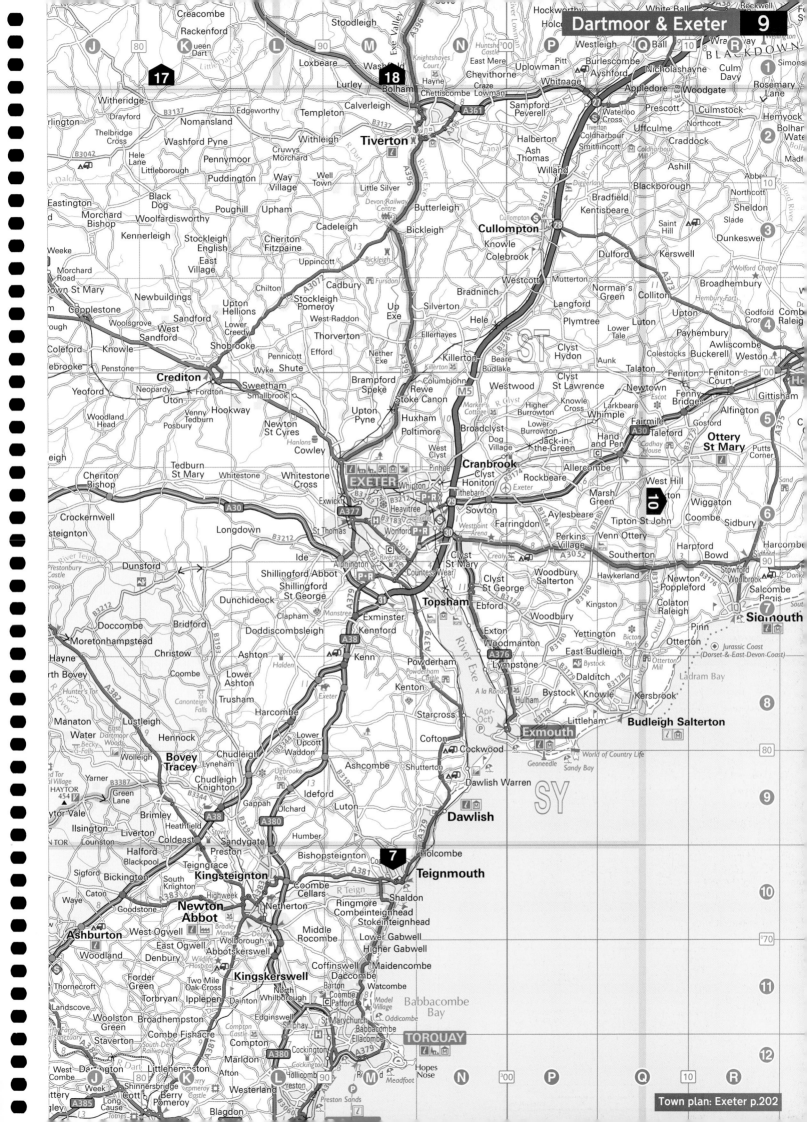

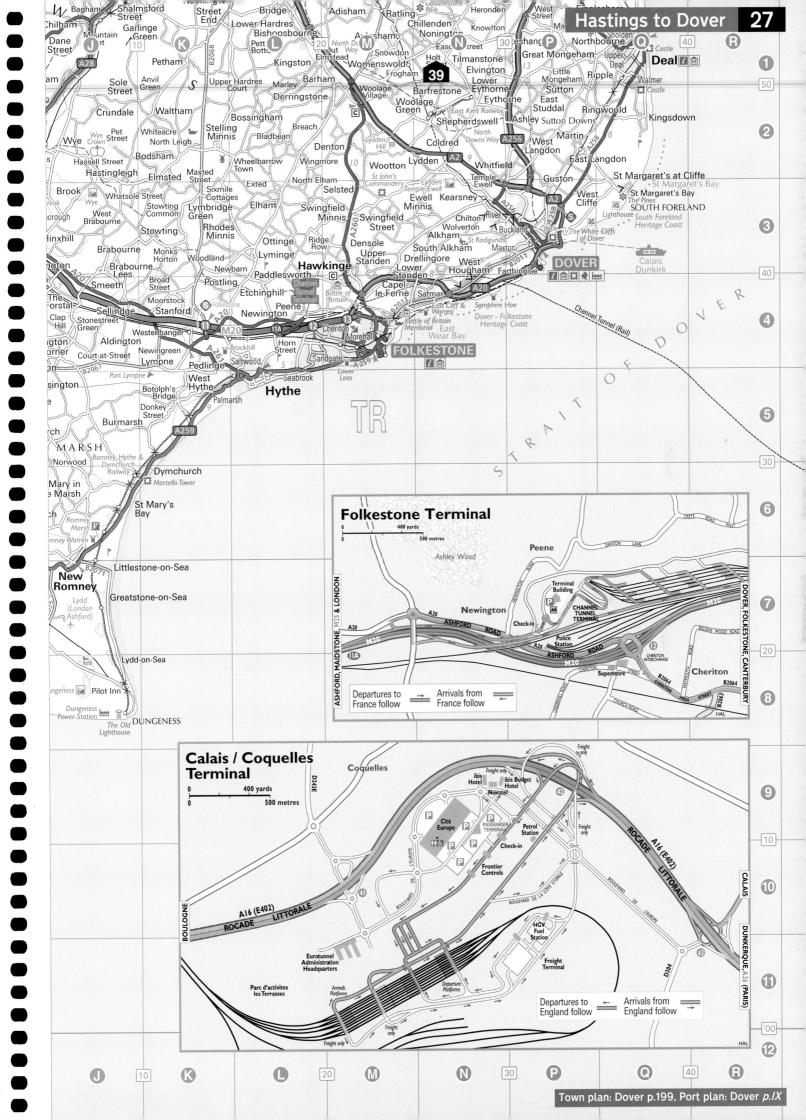

Trap

Dewi

B4310

Paxton's Tower

Golch Grove

Sarnau

Johnstown

Tre-gynwr

A40

Nantycaws

United Counties

Llanllwch

A
1
Pw...ap

Bancyfelin

B

Croesyceiliog

C
P R

D
...wmffrwd

Llanddarog

National Botanic Garden of Wales

E

A50

Penrhiwgoch

Maesybont

F

Carme

G

...rwydd

60

H

St Clears (Sanclêr)

30

Llangain

Idole

B4306

Cwmisfael

Porthyrhyd

Foelgastell

Cefneithin

A416

B4556

Cae'r bryn

Llandybie

Llanddowror

42

Llangynog

Bancycapel

Langyndeyrn

Crwbin

Drefach

Cwm-y-glo

Cross Hands

Gorslas

Penygroes

Saron

A483

Amm (Rhy

Llanddawke

A4066

Laugharne

Llanybri

Llansteffan

Pontantwn

Bancffosfelen

Cwmmawr

Tumble

Upper Tumble

Cwmgwili

Capel Hendre

Tycroes

Pentre-Gwenlais

Betws

Pantyffynnon

Llanmiloe

Llar...urnen

10

Brook

Dylan Thomas Boathouse

Castle

Broadway

Ferryside

Broadlay

River Towy

Llandyfaelog

Pontyberem

Meinciau

Pont Henri

B4306

Llannon

Pont Morlais

Sylen

A48

Garnswllt

Brodaway

2

3

Ginst Point

Wharley Point

Broadway

Castle

R Gwendraeth

Llangadog

Llansaint

Mynyddgarreg

Carway

Five Roads

Cynheidre

Horeb

Mynydd Sylen

Pont Abraham

49

S

Llanedi

Fforest

Glan-yr-afon

Craig-Fawr

Kidwelly (Cydweli)

B4317

Ffos Las

Trimsaran

Pen-y-Mynydd

Pinged

B4308

Pembrey Forest

Ffrwd Farm Mire

Cefn Sidan

Pembrey

B4311

Archddu

Dyfatty

Cwm Capel

Pwll

B4309

Cwmbach

Swiss Valley

Felinfoel

Furnace

Dafen

Pemberton

Bryn

CEFN DRUM

213

Cwm Dulais

Hendy

48

Pontarddulais

Felindre

Cra...

Waungron

Grovesend

Pontlliw

Tircoed

Swansea

Pant...

SN

41

CARMARTHEN

BAY

'00

Burry Port (Porth Tywyn)

Llanelli

Millennium Coastal Park

Machynys

Bynea

B4304

Llanelli Wetland Centre

A4138

Gorseinon

M4

17

46

Penllergaer

A48

Swansea (West)

Llwynhendy

Bwlchymyrdd

Loughor

A4240

Kingsbridge

Llangyfelach

Mynydd-Bach

Cadle

A483

La...

4

5

6

7

Burry Inlet

Salthouse Point

Penclawdd

B4295

Gowerton

Castle

A484

B4620

Fforest Fach

Waunarlwydd

Cockett

Cwmdu...

Broughton Bay

Whiteford Burrows

Llanmadoc

Landimore

Weobley Castle

Wernffrwd

Crofty

Llanmorlais

Poundffald

Three Crosses

B4296

Dunvant (Dyfnant)

A4118

Killay

Sketty

Brynmill

Burry Holms

Llangennith

Cheriton

Oldwalls

Llanrhidian

B4271

Swansea

Upper Killay

Clyne Valley

Mayals

Black-Pill

A4067

SWA (ABER

Hillend

Burry Green

Arthur's Stone

Ilston

Parc le Breos

V

West Cross

Norton

Oystermouth

Mumbles Head

Rhossili Bay

Rhossili Down

Reynoldston

Llanddewi

G O W E R

Knelston

16

Penmaen

Parkmill

Sandylane

Kittle

Murton

Pennard

Bishopston

Southgate

Caswell Bay

Langland

B4593

B4433

Mumbles Head

The Mumbles

WORMS HEAD

Visitor Centre

Middleton

Rhossili

Scurlage

A4118

Penrice

Nicholaston

Oxwich

Pwlldu Head

Gower Coast

Pilton Green

B4247

Horton

Oxwich Castle

Oxwich Point

Paviland

Port Eynon

Overton

Oxwich Green

Culver Hole

Port Eynon Point

Port Eynon Bay

Gower Heritage Coast

8

80

9

10

'70

11

12

A '30 B C 40 D E 50 F G 60 H

0   1   2   3   4   5 miles
0 1 2 3 4 5 6 7 8 kilometres

Town plan: Swansea p.230

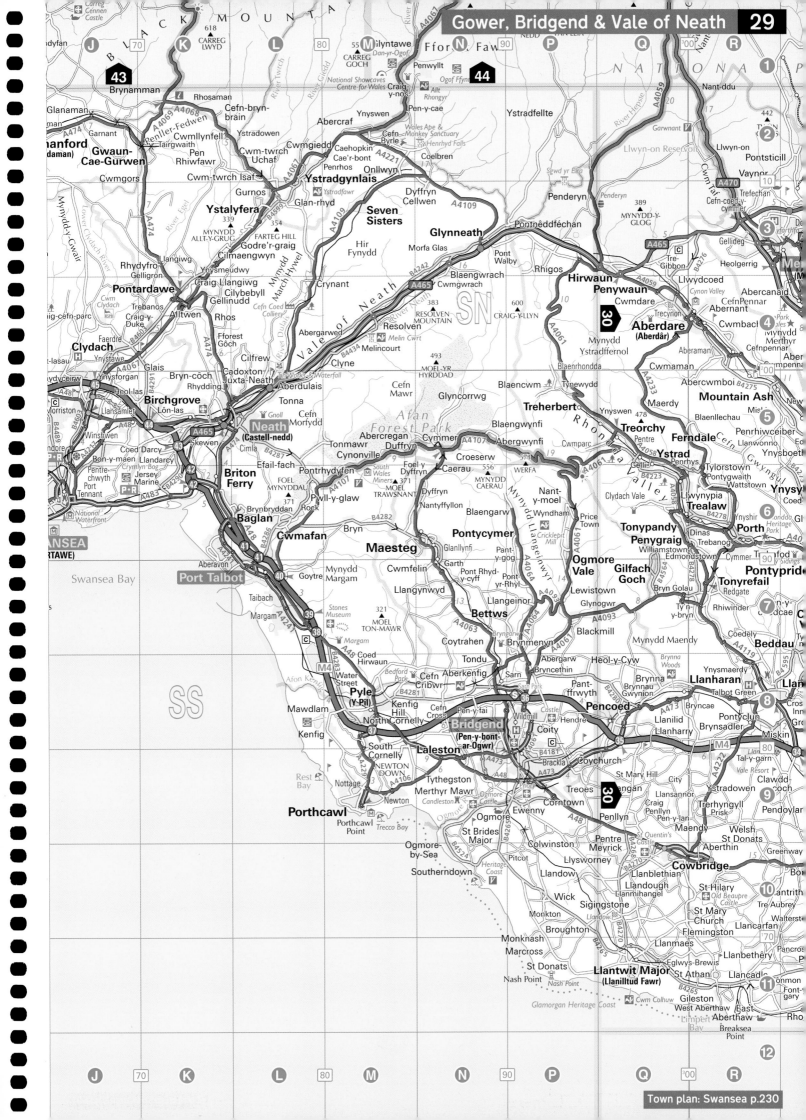

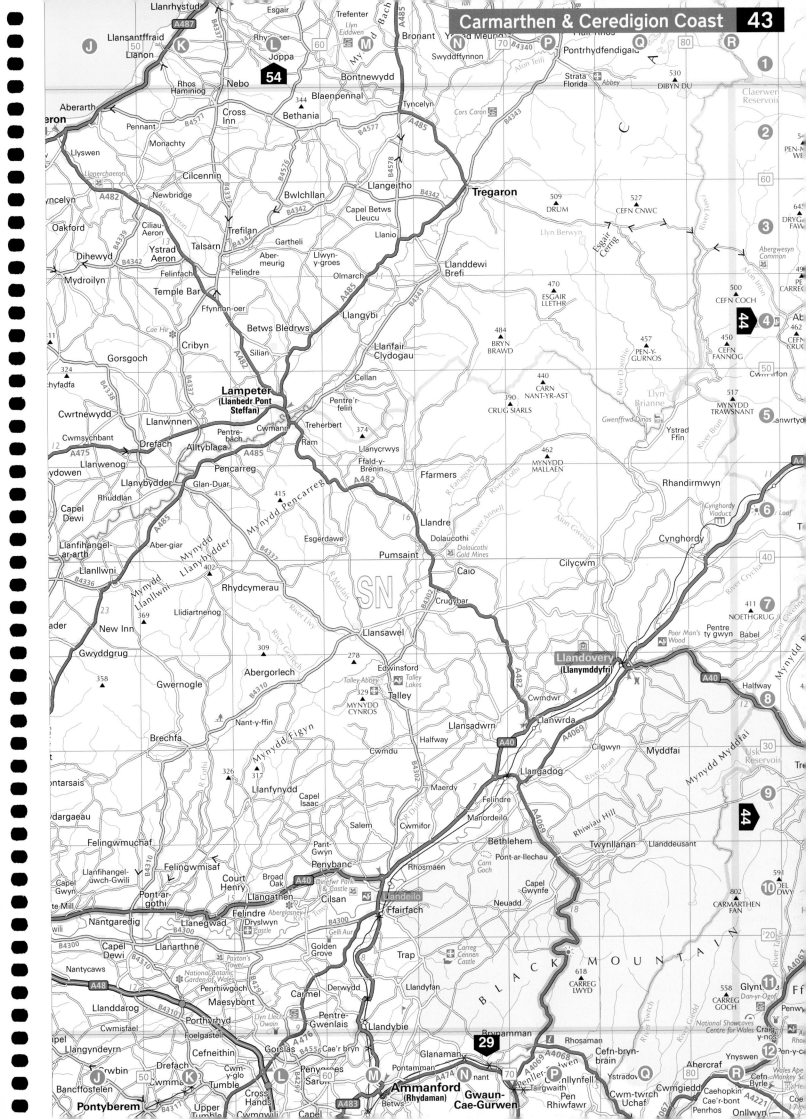

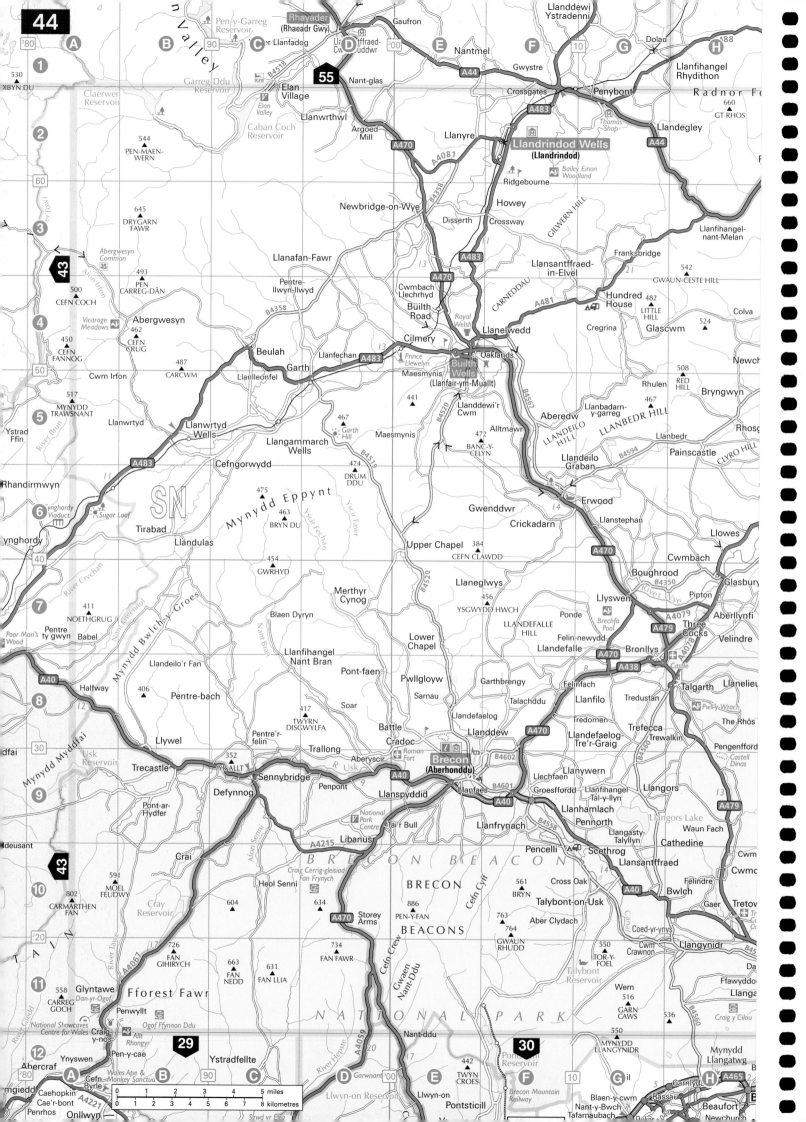

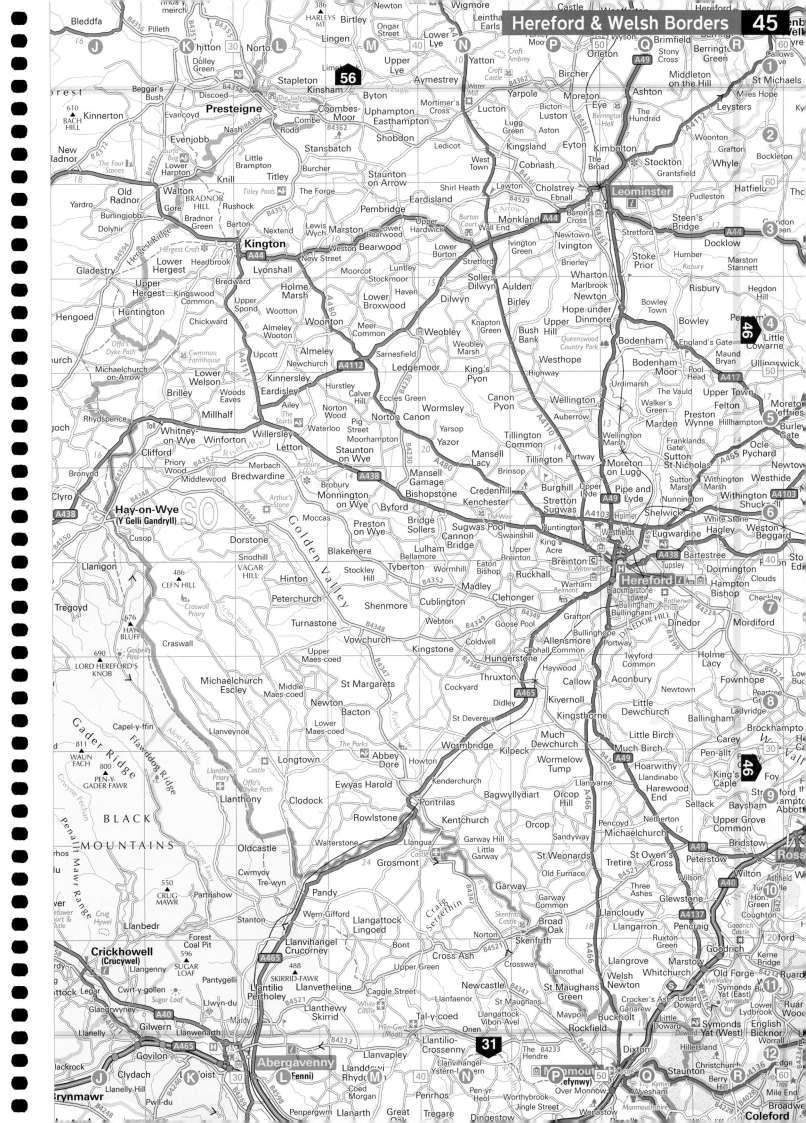

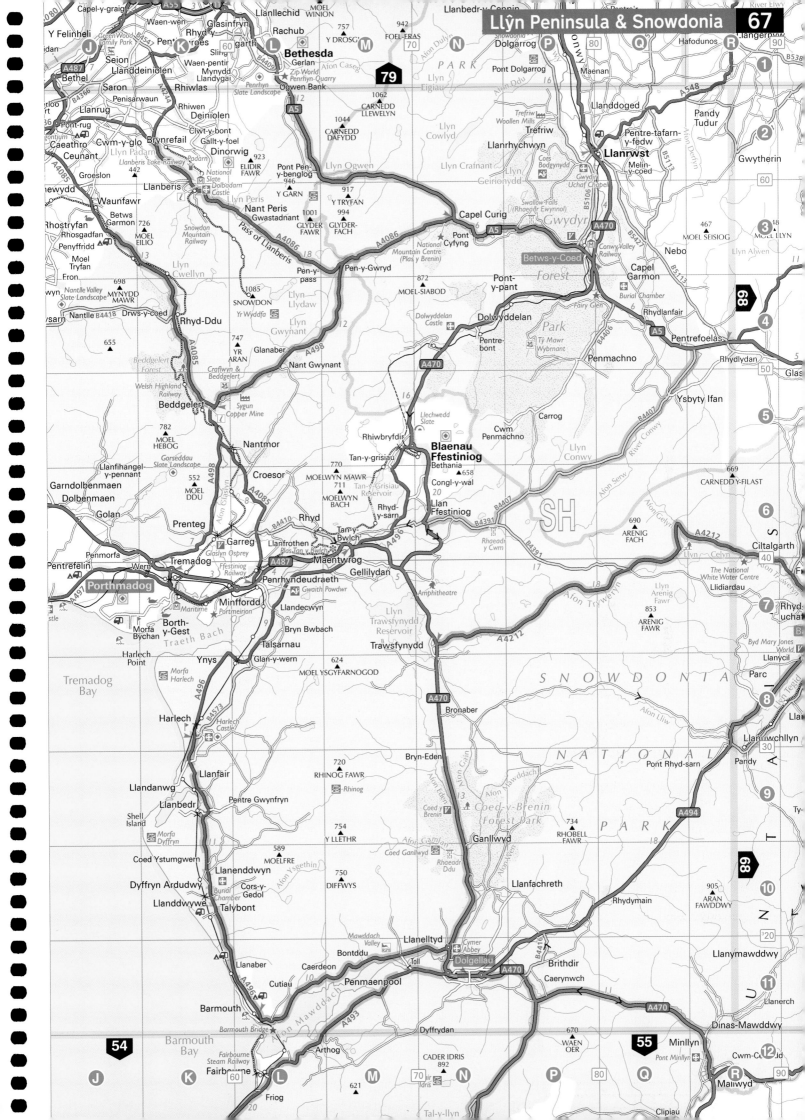

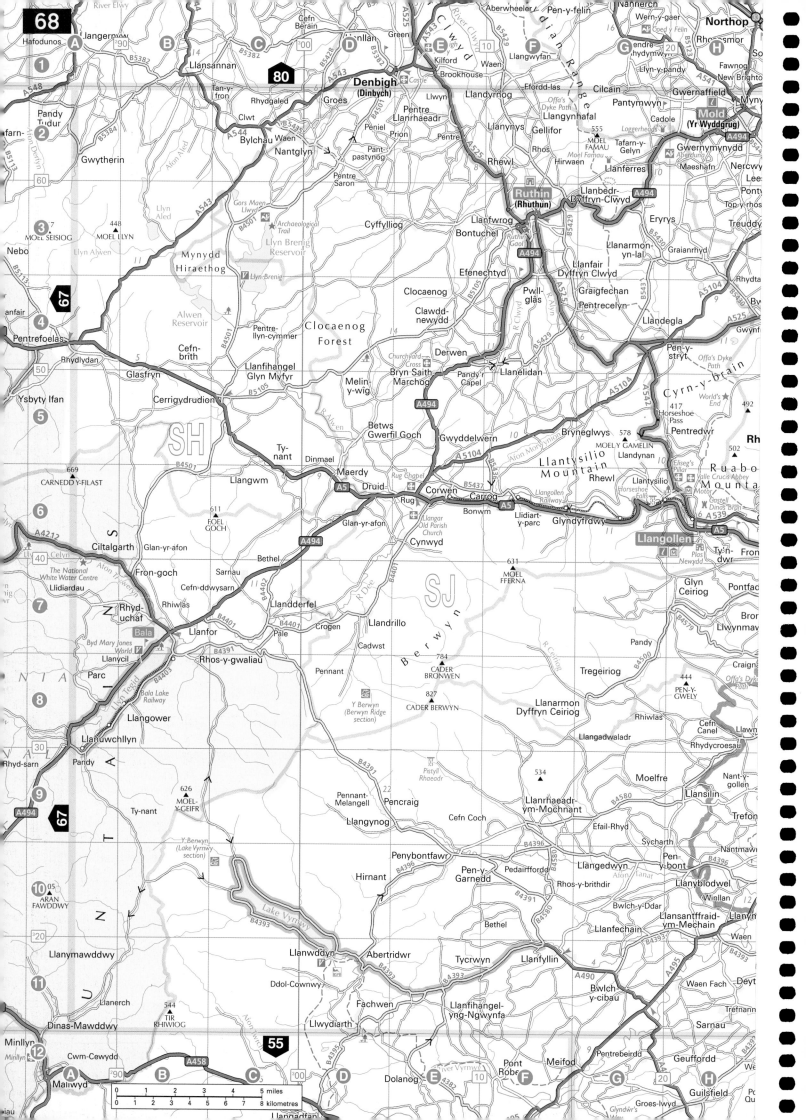

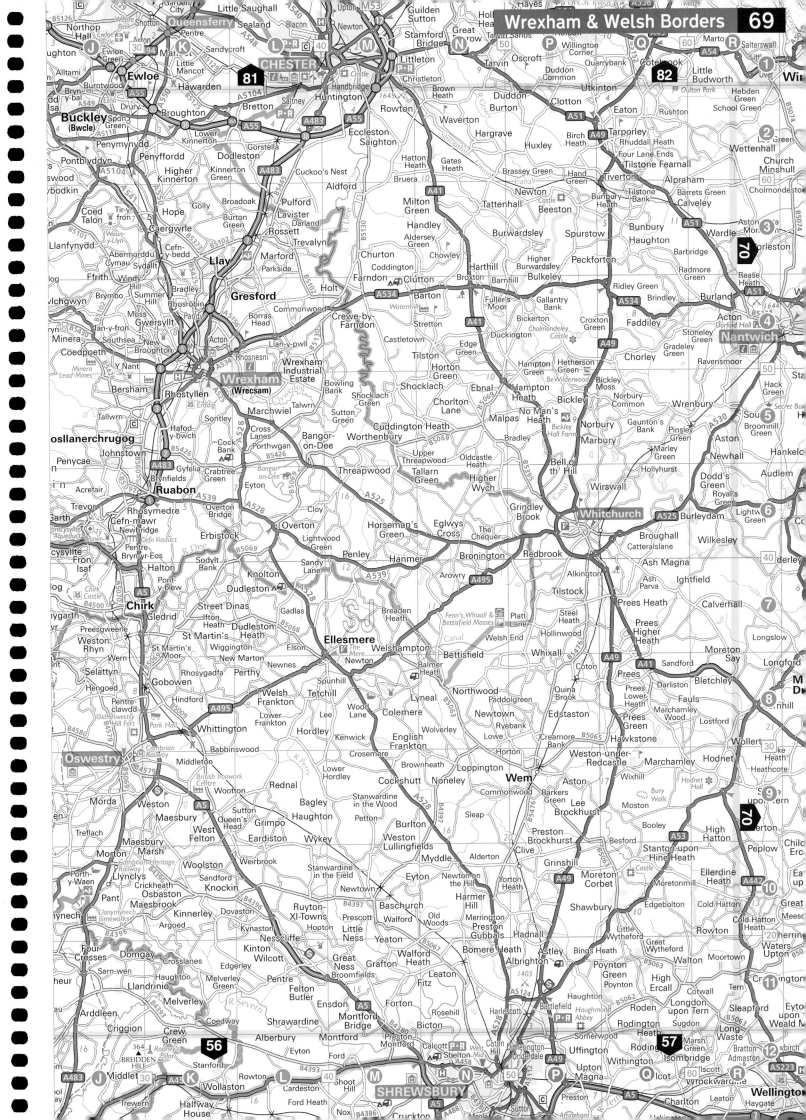

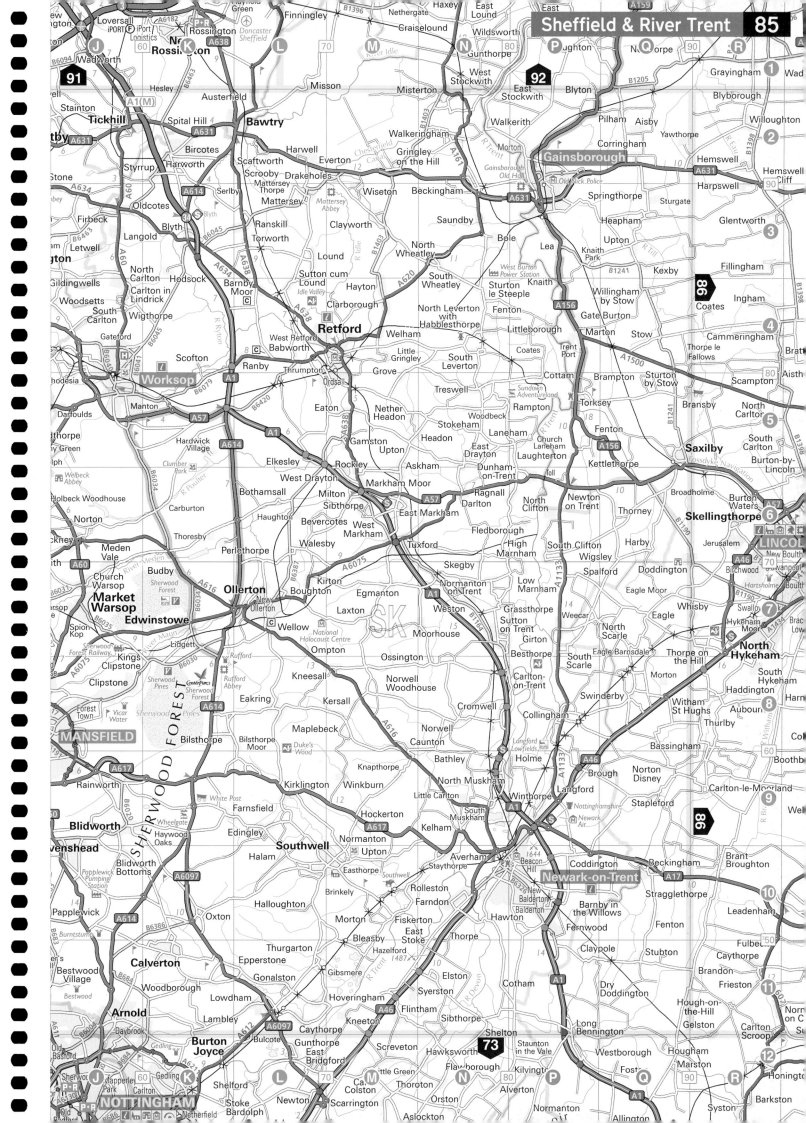

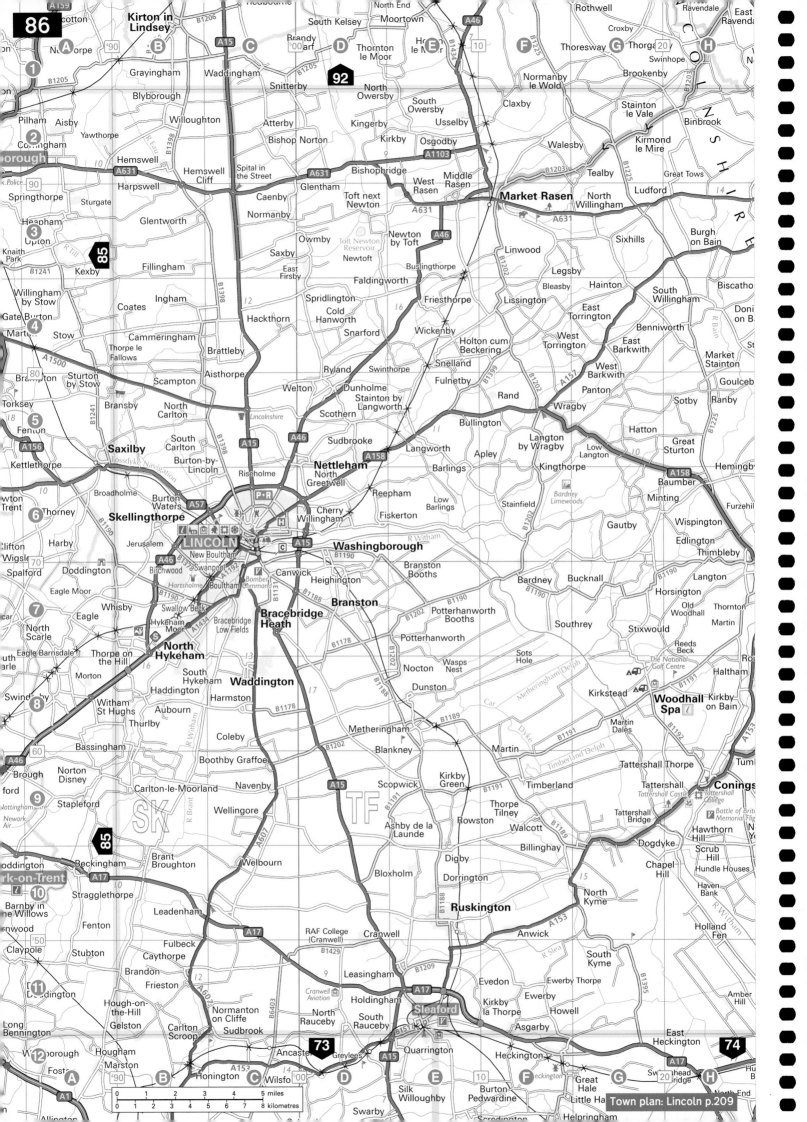

A159

Kirton in
Lindsey

B1206

North End
Moortown

A46

Rothwell

Ravendale
East
Ravendale

Croxby

Thoresway

Thorgan
Swinhope

1

cotton

NThorpe

Grayingham

B1205

Brandy
Wharf

Thornton
le Moor

Ho
le

Thoresway

B1225

Brookenby

Normanby
le Wold

2

Pilham

Aisby

Yawthorpe

Blyborough

Waddingham

Snitterby

92

North
Owersby

South
Owersby

Claxby

Stainton
le Vale

Binbrook

borough

Coningham

Willoughton

Atterby

Bishop Norton

Kingerby

Usselby

Walesby

Kirmond
le Mire

Hemswell

A631

Kirkby

Osgodby

A1103

B1203

Great Tows

3

Springthorpe

Police

90

Hemswell
Cliff

Spital in
the Street

A631

Bishopbridge

West
Rasen

Middle
Rasen

Market Rasen

North
Willingham

Ludford

14

Harpswell

Glentham

Toft next
Newton

Tealby

Sturgate

Caenby

A631

A631

Sixhills

Burgh
on Bain

Heapham

Upton

Glentworth

Owmby

Normanby

Newton
by Toft

Newtoft

Linwood

Legsby

Biscatho

Doni
on B

Knaith
Park

85

Kexby

Fillingham

Saxby

Toft Newton
Reservoir

Buslingthorpe

Bleasby

Hainton

South
Willingham

Benniworth

R Bain

Willingham
by Stow

Ingham

Spridlington
Cold
Hanworth

Friesthorpe

Lissington

East
Torrington

West
Torrington

East
Barkwith

Market
Stainton

Gate Burton

Coates

Cammeringham

Snarford

Wickenby

Holton cum
Beckering

West
Barkwith

Goulceb

4

Marton

Stow

Thorpe le
Fallows

Brattleby

Ryland

Snelland

Rand

Wragby

Panton

Sotby

Ranby

Brampton

80

Sturton
by Stow

North
Carlton

Scampton

Aisthorpe

Welton

Swinthorpe

Fulnetby

B1399

A157

Hatton

B1225

Great
Sturton

Torksey

Bransby

A1500

Dunholme

Stainton by
Langworth

Bullington

Langton
by Wragby

Low
Langton

5

Fenton

A156

Saxilby

South
Carlton

Scothern

Apley

A158

Baumber

Fossdyke Navigation

Kettlethorpe

Burton-by-
Lincoln

Riseholme

Nettleham

Langworth

Kingthorpe

Minting

Wispington

6

wton
Trent

Broadholme

Burton
Waters

A57

North
Greetwell

Reepham

Low
Barlings

Stainfield

Bardney
Limewoods

Hemingb

Edlington

Thorney

Skellingthorpe

Barlings

Gautby

Furzehill

Thimbleby

Harby

Jerusalem

LINCOLN

Cherry
Willingham

Fiskerton

R Witham

7

Clifton
Wigsle

70

A46

New Boultham
Swanpool

C

A15

Washingborough

B1190

Branston
Booths

Bardney

Bucknall

B1190

Langton

Spalford

Doddington

Birchwood

Boultham
Hartsholme

Bomber
Command

Canwick

Heighington

Branston

B1202

Potterhanworth
Booths

Horsington

Old
Woodhall

Thornton

Eagle Moor

B1190

Swallow Beck

Bracebridge
Heath

Potterhanworth

Southrey

Stixwould

Reeds
Beck

car

North
Scarle

Whisby

Hykeham
Moor

A1434

Bracebridge
Low Fields

B1178

Nocton

Wasps
Nest

The National
Golf Centre

Haltham

Eagle Barnsdale

arle

Thorpe on
the Hill

North
Hykeham

Morton

South
Hykeham

Dunston

Sots
Hole

Kirkstead

Woodhall
Spa

Kirkby
on Bain

8

Swinderby

Haddington

Harmston

Metheringham Delph

Metheringham

B1189

Martin
Dales

B1192

A153

Witham
St Hughs

Auburn

B1178

Martin

B1191

A46

60

Thurlby

Coleby

Blankney

Tattershall Thorpe

Brough

Bassingham

Boothby Graffoe

Nocton

B1202

Kirkby
Green

Timberland

Tattershall

Conings

ford

Norton
Disney

Carlton-le-Moorland

Navenby

A15

Scopwick

Thorpe
Tilney

Tattershall Castle

Battle of Brita
Memorial Flig

Nottinghamshire
Air

Stapleford

SK

Wellingore

A607

Rowston

Martin

B1189

Tattershall
Bridge

Hawthorn
Hill

Newark

9

85

Beckingham

Brant
Broughton

Welbourn

Ashby de la
Laude

Walcott

Dogdyke

Scrub
Hill

Hundle Houses

oddington

A17

ork-on-Trent

Stragglethorpe

Bloxholm

Billinghay

Chapel
Hill

Haven
Bank

R Witham

10

Barnby in
he Willows

Leadenham

Dorrington

North
Kyme

Holland
Fen

nwood

Fenton

A17

RAF College
(Cranwell)

Cranwell

Anwick

A153

15

Claypole

50

Stubton

Fulbeck

Caythorpe

B1429

Leasingham

Evedon

South
Kyme

Ewerby Thorpe

Ewerby

B1395

Amber
Hill

11

Doddington

Hough-on-
the-Hill

Brandon

Frieston

12

Cranwell
Aviation

9

A17

Holdingham

Sleaford

Kirkby
la Thorpe

Howell

East
Heckington

Long
Bennington

Hougham

Gelston

A607

Normanton
on Cliffe

North
Rauceby

South
Rauceby

Asgarby

12

Wborough

Foss

Marston

90

Carlton
Scroop

Sudbrook

B6403

73

Ancaster

Greylees

A15

Quarrington

Heckington

A17

H

A1

A

Honington

B

A153

Wilsfo

C

500

D

Silk
Willoughby

E

Swarby

F

eckington

Great
Hale

Burton
Pedwardine

Little Ha

G

Swi
head
ridge

20

74

North End

H

A17

0   1   2   3   4   5 miles
0 1 2 3 4 5 6 7 8 kilometres

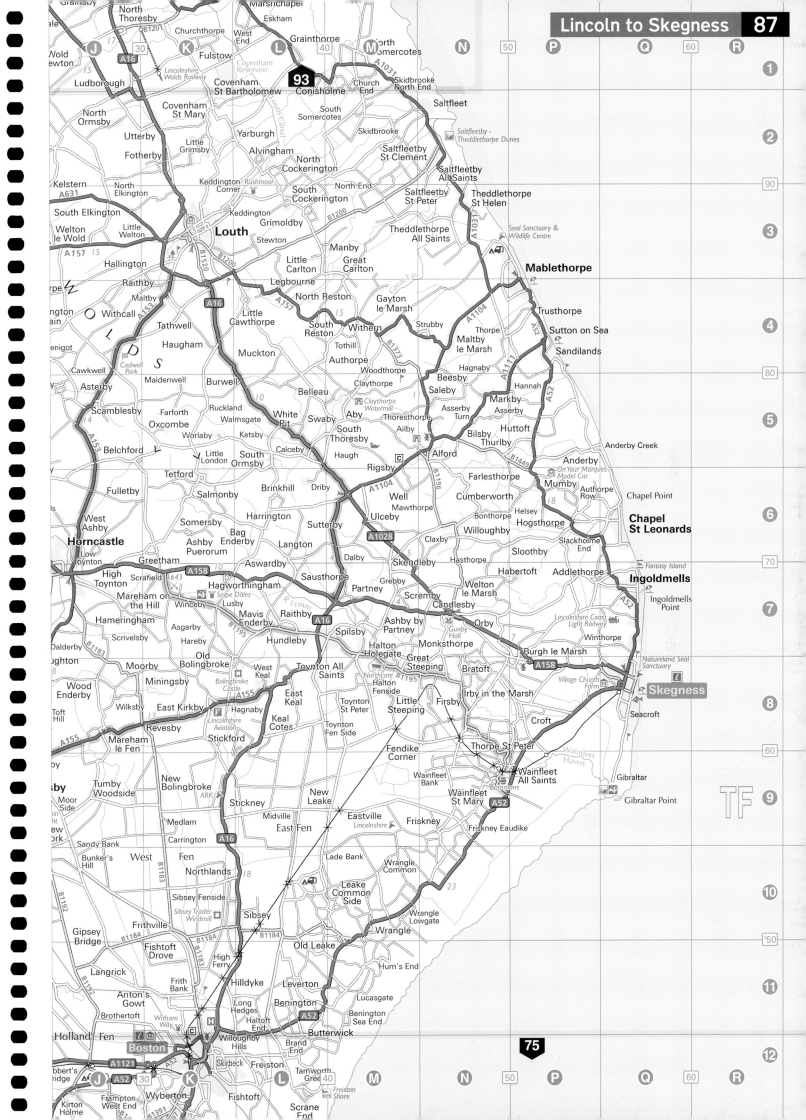

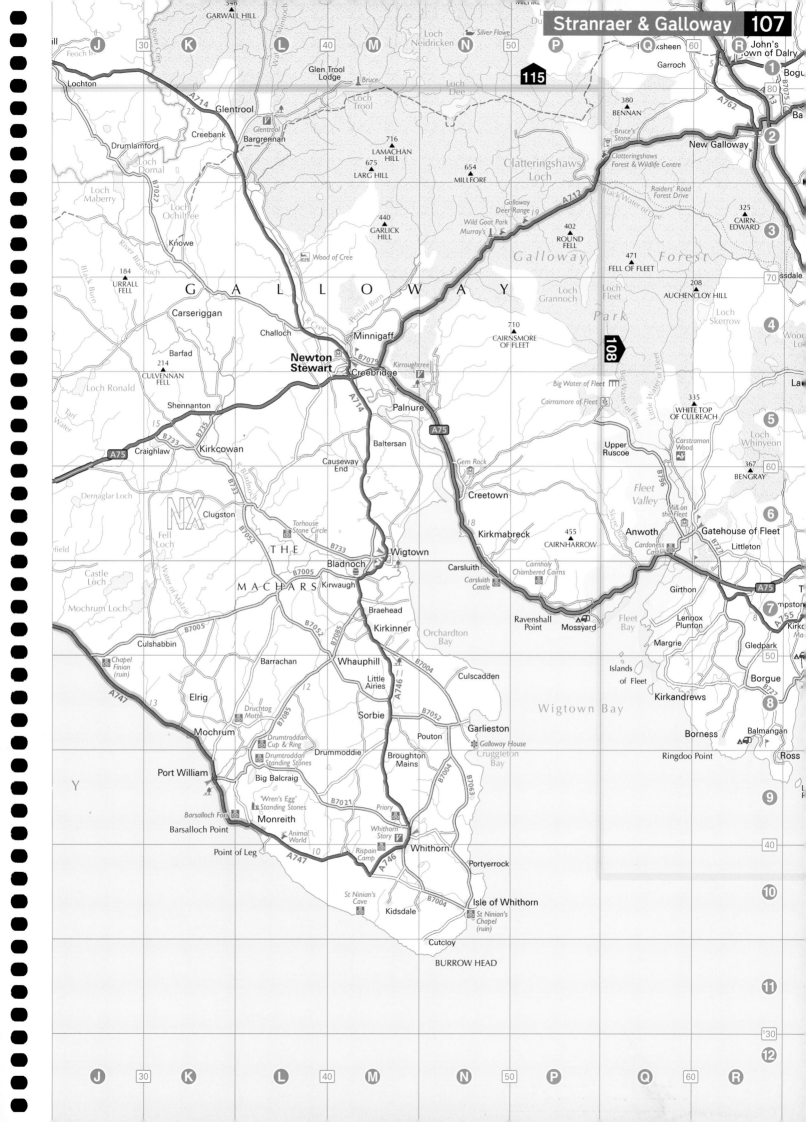

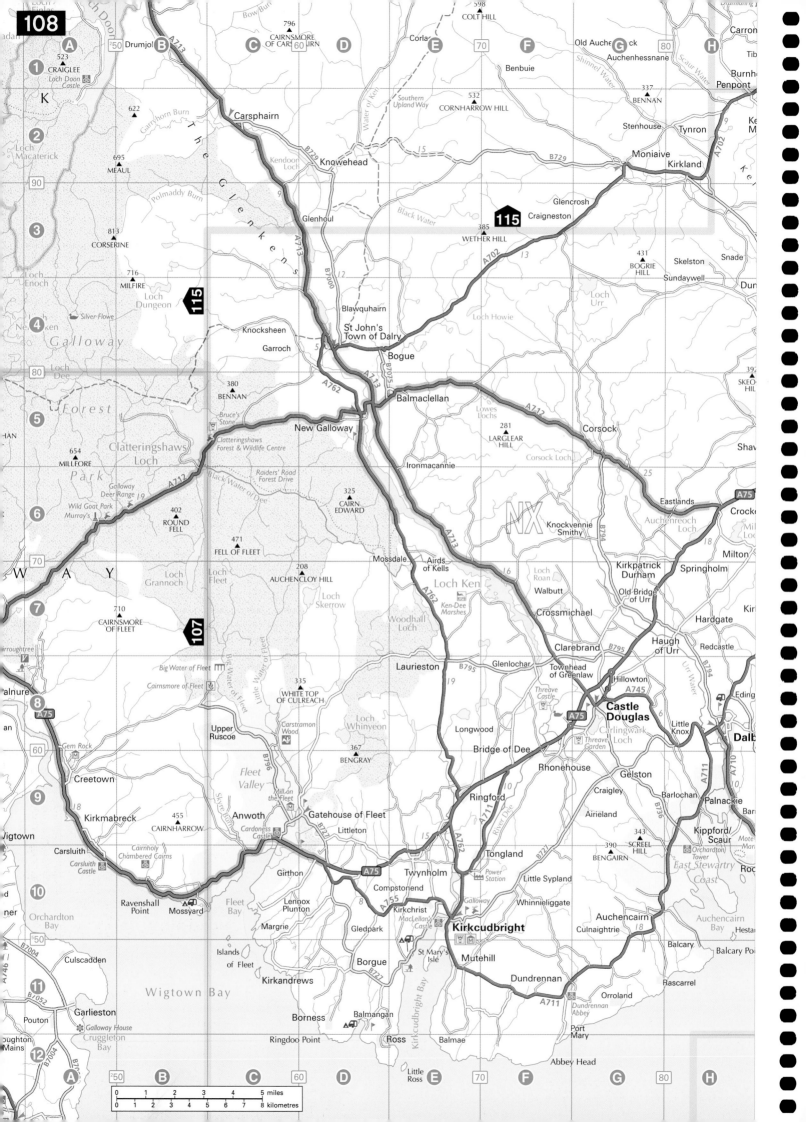

A B C D E F G H

1 523 ▲ CRAIGLEE
Loch Doon Castle
K
A713
50 Drumjoł
A713
Cairnsmore of Cars[H]urn
796
598 COLT HILL
Corlae
70
Old Auchen[Geck]
Auchenhessnane
80
Penpont
Burnh[ead]

2 Loch Macaterick
622 ▲
90
Garryhorn Burn
The Glenkens
Carsphairn
Southern Upland Way
Benbuie
CORNHARROW HILL 532
Shinnel Water
Stenhouse
Tynron
337 ▲ BENNAN
A702

Loch Enoch
695 ▲ MEAUL
Kendoon Loch
B729
Knowehead
Water of Ken
15
B729
Moniaive
Kirkland

3 813 ▲ CORSERINE
Polmaddy Burn
Glenhoul
Black Water
WETHER HILL 385 ▲
115
A702
13
Craigneston
Glencrosh
431 ▲ BOGRIE HILL
Skelston
Snade
Sundaywell

4 New [K]en
716 ▲ MILFIRE
Loch Dungeon
115
Knocksheen
Galloway
Silver Flowe
Garroch
B7000
12
Blawquhairn
St John's Town of Dalry
5
9
Loch Howie

5 Loch Dee
80
Forest
BENNAN 380 ▲
Bruce's Stone
Clatteringshaws Forest & Wildlife Centre
New Galloway
A762
A713
B7075
Bogue
Balmaclellan
A712
Lowes Lochs
392 ▲ SKEO[CH] HILL

Clatteringshaws Loch
654 ▲ MILLFORE
Park
A712
Black Water of Dee
Raiders' Road Forest Drive
325 ▲ CAIRN EDWARD
LARGLEAR HILL 281 ▲
Corsock
Ironmacannie
A712
Corsock Loch
25
Eastlands
A75
Crock[et]

6 Galloway Deer Range
Wild Goat Park
Murray's
402 ▲ ROUND FELL
19
471 ▲ FELL OF FLEET
Mossdale
Airds of Kells
NX
A713
16
Knockvennie Smithy
Auchenreoch Loch
B79A
18
Milton

7 70
W A Y
CAIRNSMORE OF FLEET 710 ▲
Loch Grannoch
Loch Fleet
AUCHENCLOY HILL 208 ▲
Loch Skerrow
107
Loch Ken
A762
Woodhall Loch
Ken-Dee Marshes
Loch Roan
Walbutt
Kirkpatrick Durham
Old Bridge of Urr
Springholm

8 A75
Big Water of Fleet
Cairnsmore of Fleet
335 ▲ WHITE TOP OF CULREACH
Laurieston
B795
Glenlochar
Clarebrand
B795
Crossmichael
Townhead of Greenlaw
Haugh of Urr
Redcastle
B794
Kir[k]

9 60
Gem Rock
Carstramon Wood
Upper Ruscoe
367 ▲ BENGRAY
Loch Whinyeon
Longwood
Bridge of Dee
Threave Castle
A75
Hillowton
A745
Castle Douglas
Carlingwark Loch
Threave Garden
Little Knox
6
Eding
Dalb[e]

10 Creetown
18
Kirkmabreck
455 ▲ CAIRNHARROW
B796
Skyre Burn
Fleet Valley
Mill on the Fleet
Gatehouse of Fleet
Littleton
15
A755
A762
Ringford
A711
River Dee
10
Rhonehouse
Craigley
Gelston
Airieland
B736
Barlochan
Palnackie
A711
A710
Bar[r]
343 ▲ SCREEL HILL
Kippford/ Scaur
Mote [Mar]

11 Wigtown
Carsluith
Carsluith Castle
Cairnholy Chambered Cairns
Anwoth
Cardoness Castle
Ravenshall Point
Mossyard
A75
Lennox Plunton
Margrie
Girthon
Twynholm
Compstonend
Kirkchrist
MacLellan's Castle
Tongland
Power Station
Galloway
Whinnieliggate
BENGAIRN 390 ▲
Auchencairn
Culnaightrie
18
Orchardton Tower
East Stewartry Coast
Ro[ck]

12 Orchardton Bay
B7004
Culscadden
Islands of Fleet
Fleet Bay
Gledpark
Borgue
B727
St Mary's Isle
Kirkcudbright
Mutehill
Dundrennan
A711
Auchencairn Bay
Balcary
Balcary Po[int]
Hestan

A746
B7004
11 B7052
Pouton
Garlieston
Galloway House
Cruggleton Bay
[B]oughton Mains
B7[0]04
B7[]
12 Wigtown Bay
Kirkandrews
Balmangan
Borness
Ringdoo Point
Ross
Balmae
Kirkcudbright Bay
Little Ross
Port Mary
Dundrennan Abbey
Orroland
Rascarrel
Abbey Head

A B C D E F G H

50 60 70 80

0 1 2 3 4 5 miles
0 1 2 3 4 5 6 7 8 kilometres

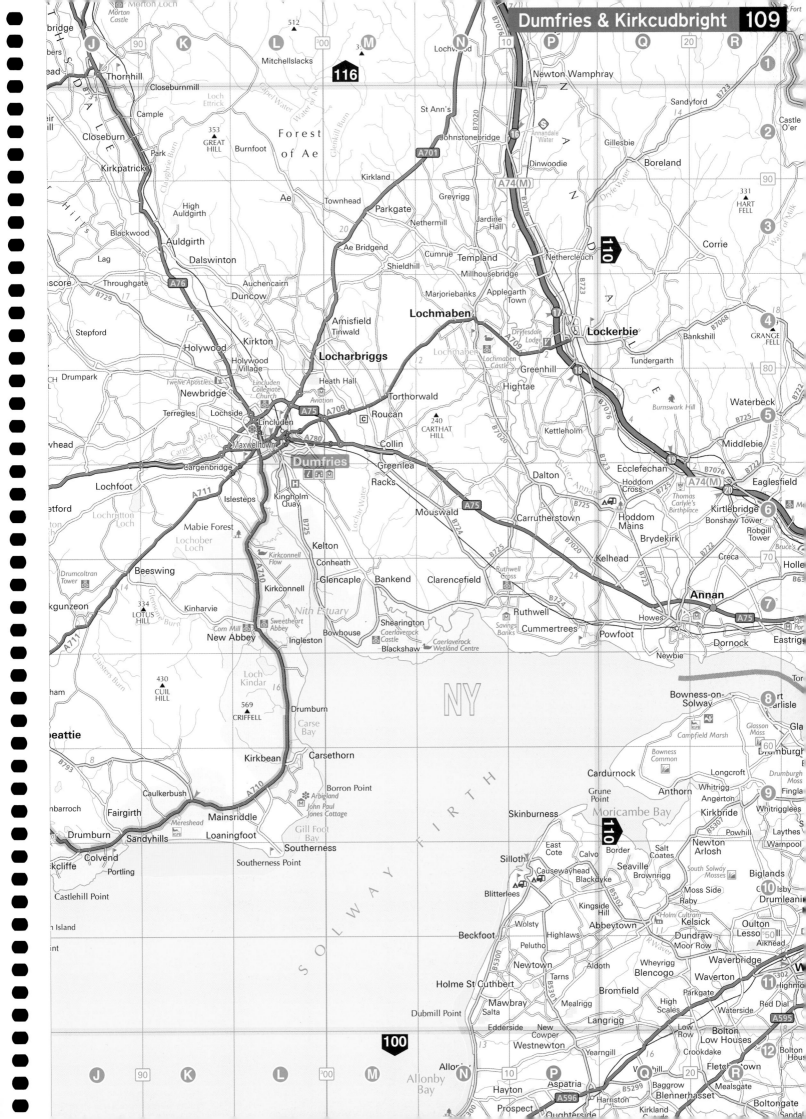

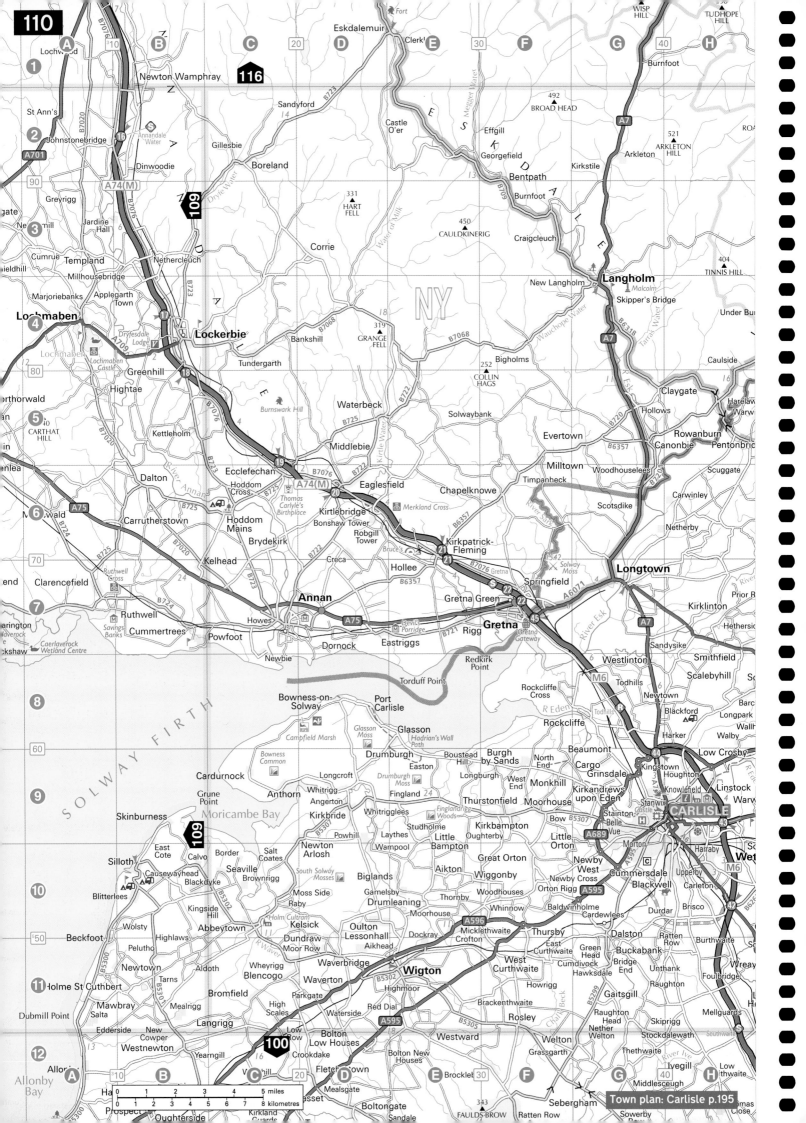

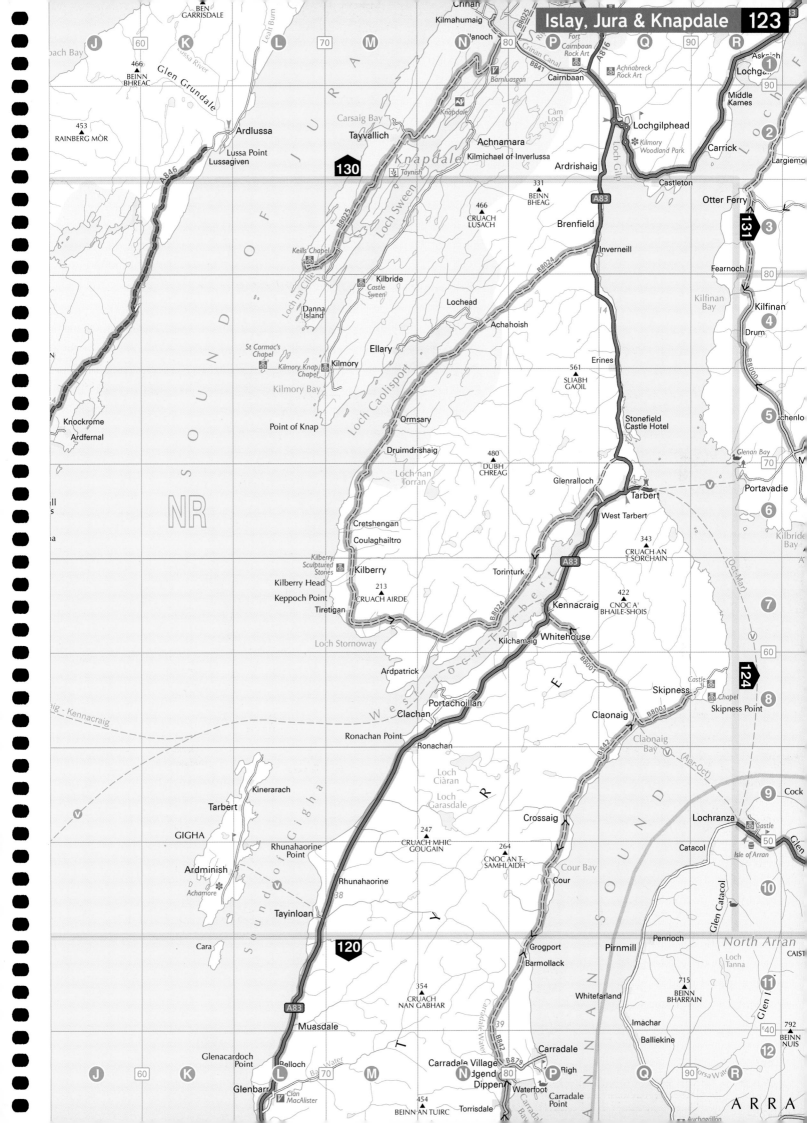

BEN GARRISDALE

Crinan

Kilmahumaig

Ilanoch

B8025

80

Fort Cairnbaan Rock Art

Achnabreck Rock Art

A816

Asknish

Lochg...

J 60 K L 70 M N 80 P Q 90 R

1

Cairnbaan

Lochgilphead

Middle Kames

2

466 BEINN BHREAC

Glen Grundale

Lussa River

Leoll Burn

Carsaig Bay

Knapdale

B841

Kilmory Woodland Park

Carrick

Largiemo...

Ardlussa

Taivallich

Achnamara

Ardrishaig

Castleton

90

453 RAINBERG MÒR

Lussa Point

Lussagiven

Kilmichael of Inverlussa

A83

Otter Ferry

3

131

Knapdale

130

Taynish

331 BEINN BHEAG

Brenfield

Inverneill

Fearnoch

80

466 CRUACH LUSACH

Kilfinan Bay

Kilfinan

4

Keills Chapel

B8025

Loch Sween

B8024

Drum

Loch na Cille

Kilbride

Castle Sween

Lochead

Achahoish

Erines

B8000

Danna Island

St Cormac's Chapel

561 SLIABH GAOIL

5

Ellary

chenlo

Kilmory

Kilmory Knap Chapel

Ormsary

Stonefield Castle Hotel

Glenan Bay

70

Kilmory Bay

Point of Knap

Druimdrishaig

480 DUBH CHREAG

Glenralloch

Portavadie

V

NR

Loch nan Torran

Tarbert

6

Cretshengan

West Tarbert

343 CRUACH AN T-SORCHAIN

Kilbride Bay

Coulaghailtro

Kilberry Sculptured Stones

A83

Torinturk

Kilberry

422 CNOC A' BHAILE-SHOIS

7

Kilberry Head

Keppoch Point

213 CRUACH AIRDE

B8024

Kennacraig

V

Tiretigan

Whitehouse

60

Loch Stornoway

Kilchamaig

B8001

124

Ardpatrick

West Loch Tarbert

Skipness

Castle

8

Portachoillan

Chapel

Skipness Point

Craig - Kennacraig

V

Clachan

Claonaig

B8001

Ronachan Point

Claonaig Bay

V (Apr-Oct)

Ronachan

9

Loch Ciàran

Crossaig

Cock

Kinerarach

Loch Garasdale

Lochranza

Castle

Tarbert

R

50

Glen

GIGHA

247 CRUACH MHIC GOUGAIN

Catacol

Isle of Arran

Rhunahaorine Point

264 CNOC AN T-SAMHLAIDH

Cour Bay

Glen Catacol

10

Ardminish

V

Cour

Achamore

Sound of Gigha

Rhunahaorine

38

North Arran

Loch Tanna

Cara

120

Grogport

Pirnmill

Penrioch

11

Barmollack

715 BEINN BHARRAIN

CAIST

Tayinloan

A83

Muasdale

354 CRUACH NAN GABHAR

Whitefarland

Imachar

792 BEINN NUIS

12

Glenacardoch Point

Belloch

Carradale

Balliekine

Glenbarr

Clan MacAlister

Carradale Village

...dgend

Righ

Carradale Point

J 60 K 70 L M N 80 P Q 90 R

454 BEINN AN TUIRC

Dippen

Waterfoot

A R R A

Torrisdale

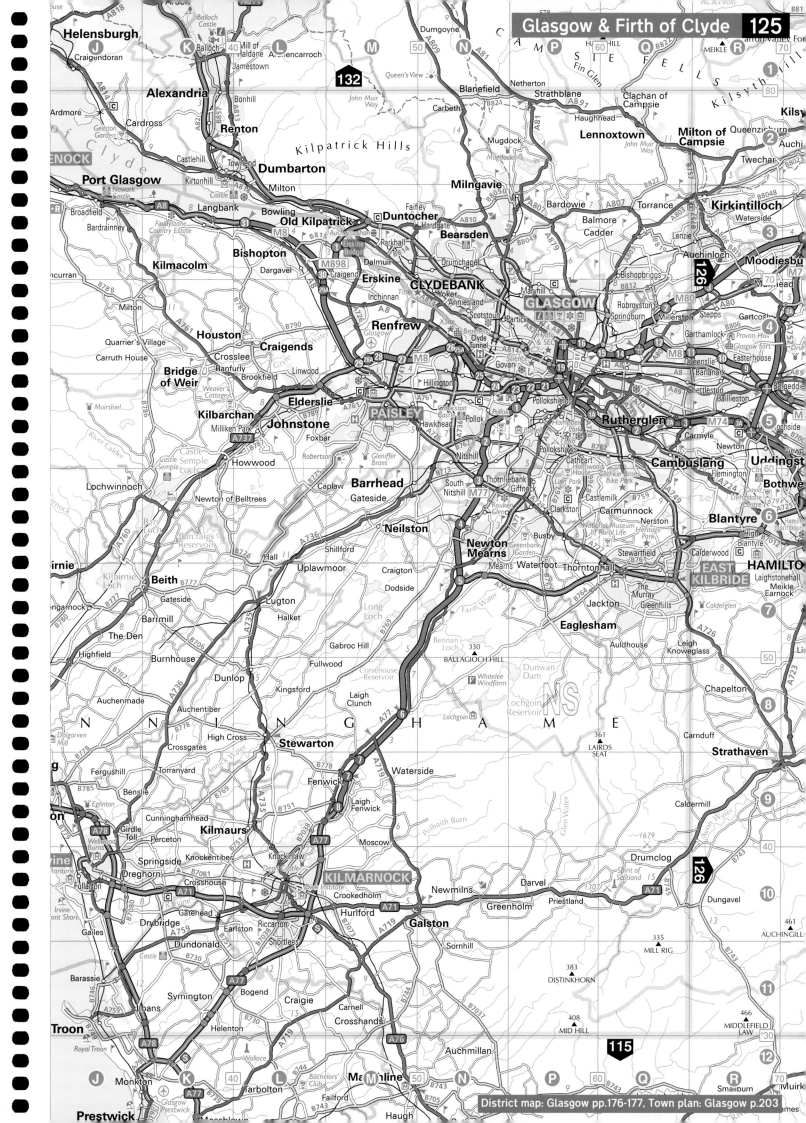

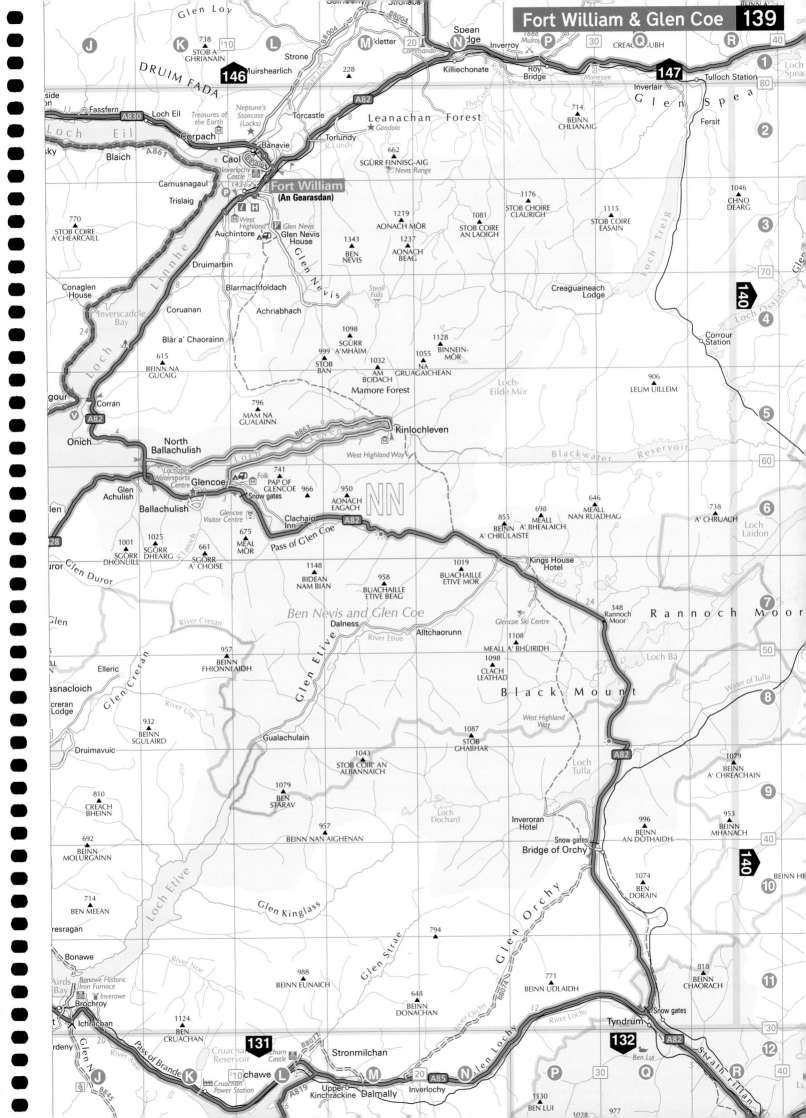

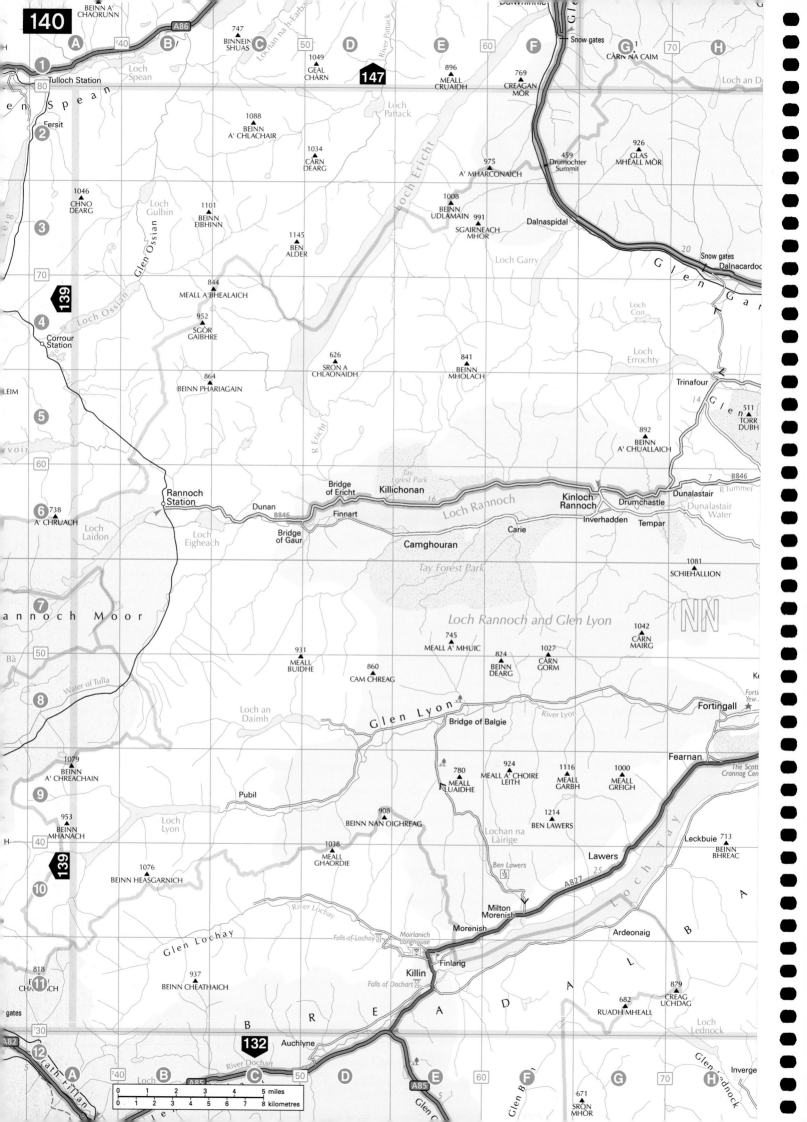

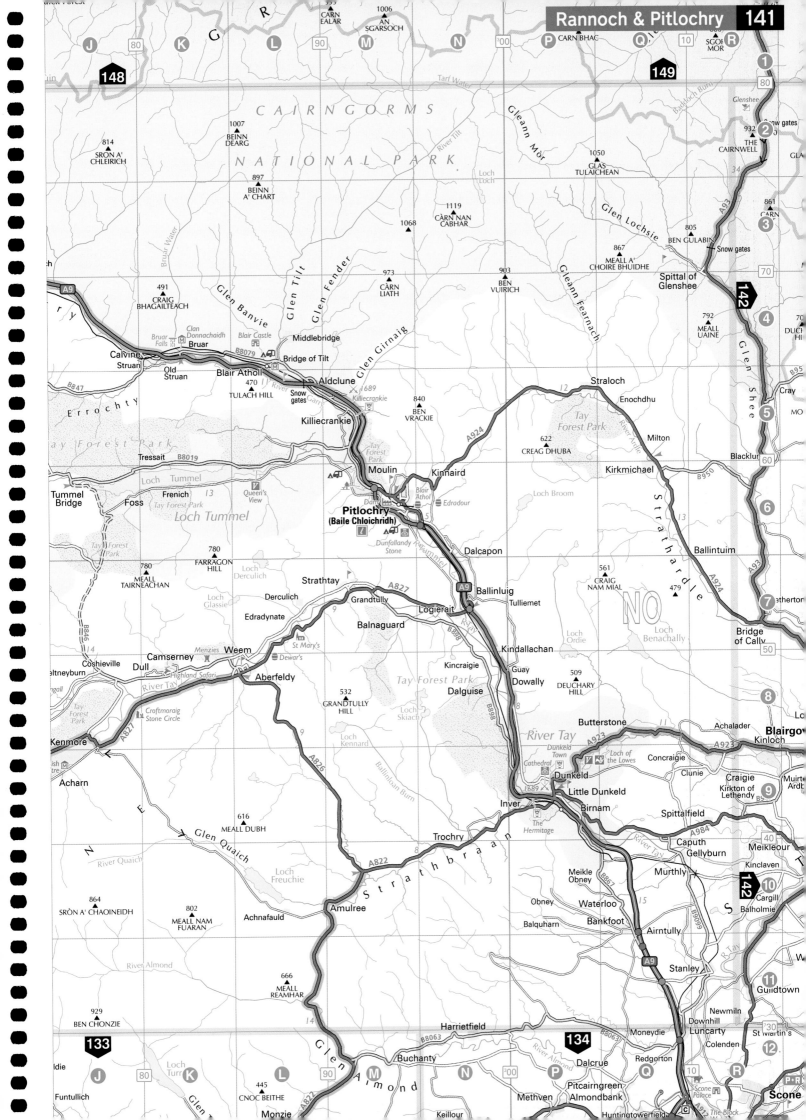

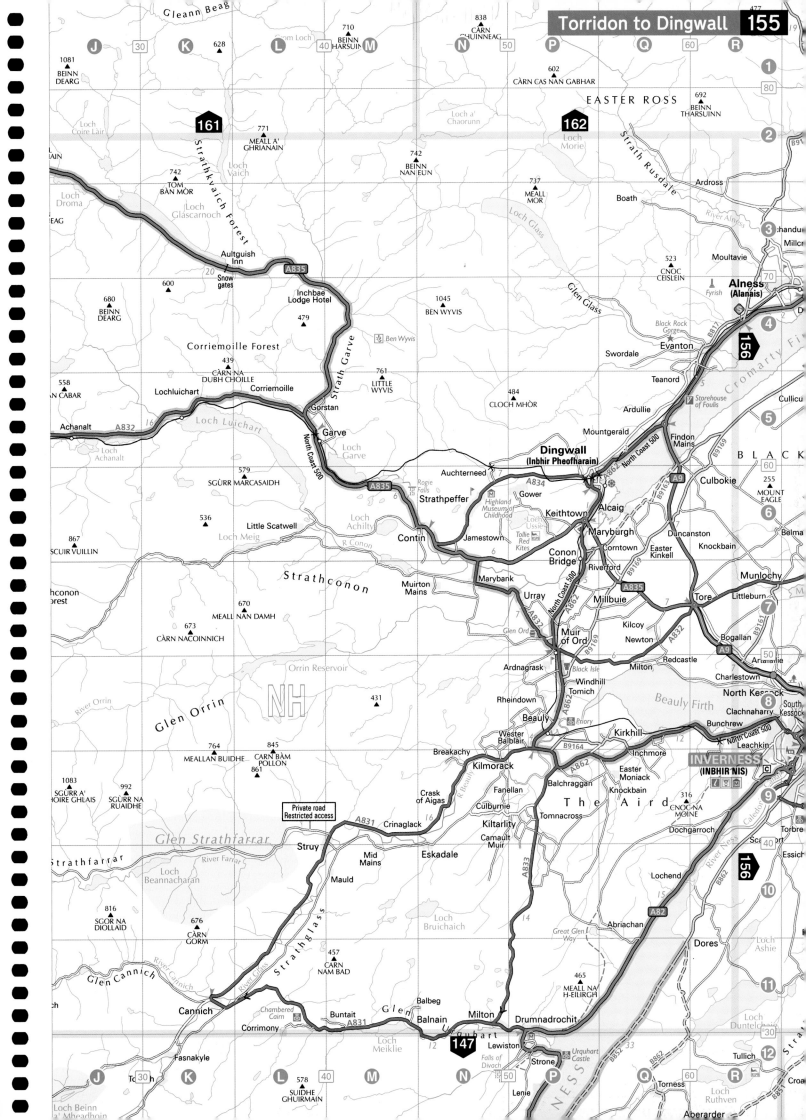

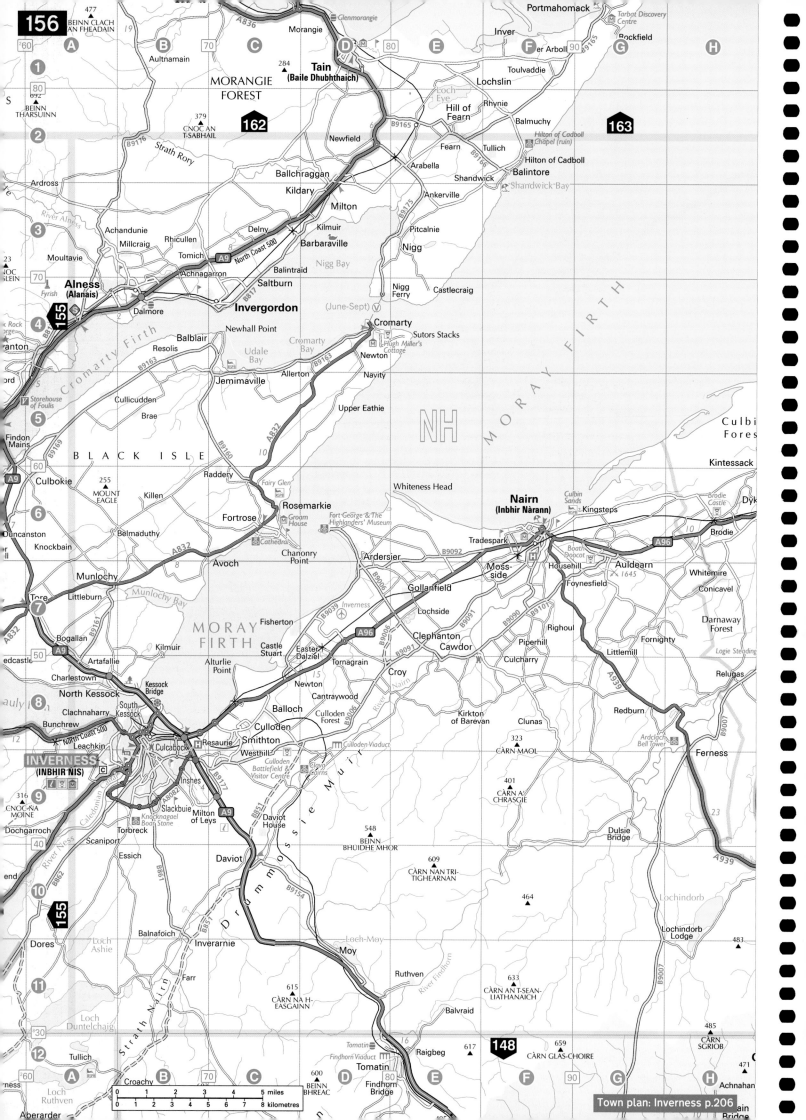

Town plan: Inverness p.206

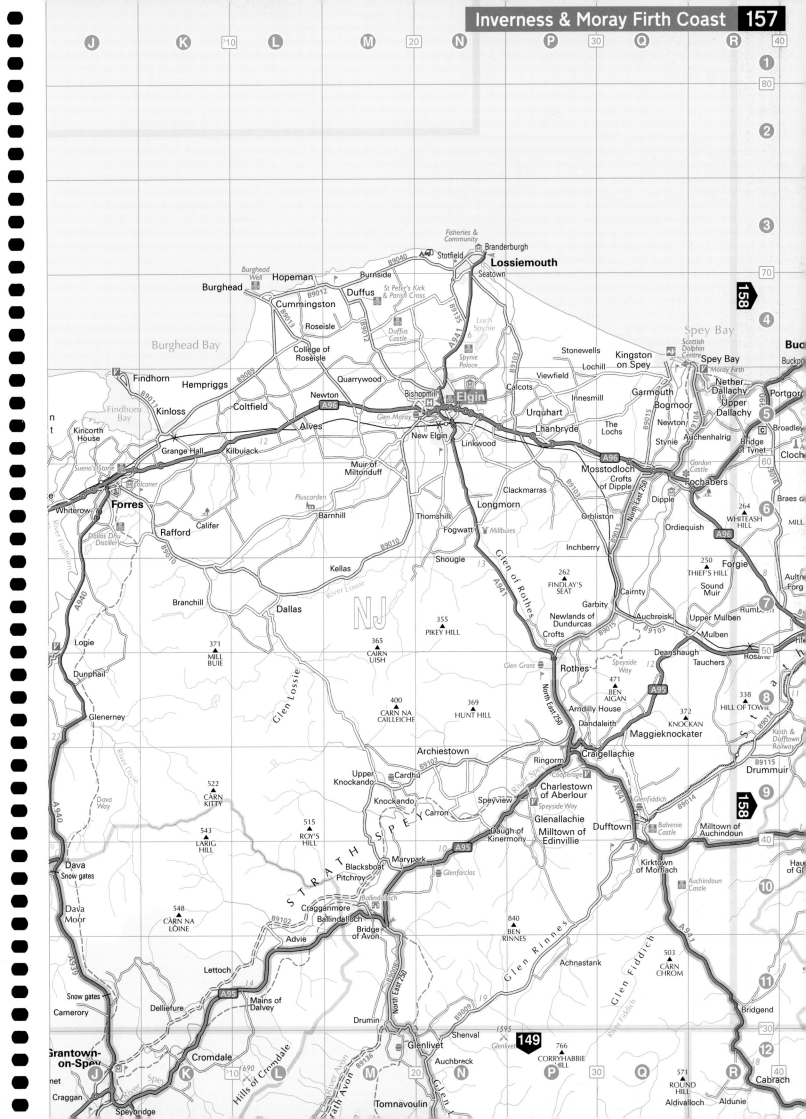

Map grid columns: J K L M N P Q R
Map grid rows: 1 2 3 4 5 6 7 8 9 10 11 12

`158`

`158`

`149`

Burghead Bay
Findhorn Bay
Spey Bay
Moray Firth

Fisheries & Community
Branderburgh
Stotfield
Lossiemouth
Seatown
B9040
Hopeman
Burnside
Burghead Well
Burghead
Duffus
St Peter's Kirk & Parish Cross
B9012
Cummingston
Roseisle
Duffus Castle
B9013
B9012
Loch Spynie
B9135
College of Roseisle
Spynie Palace
Stonewells
Lochill
Kingston on Spey
Scottish Dolphin Centre
Spey Bay
Buc
B9089
Quarrywood
Viewfield
Garmouth
Nether Dallachy
Portgo
Findhorn
Hempriggs
Newton
Bishopmill
Elgin
Calcots
Urquhart
Bogmoor
Upper Dallachy
Broadley
A96
Innesmill
Newton
B9104
Kinloss
Coltfield
Alves
Glen Moray
Lhanbryde
The Lochs
Stynie
Auchenhalrig
Bridge of Tynet
Cloch
Kincorth House
Grange Hall
Kilbuiack
New Elgin
Linkwood
B9015
Gordon Castle
Mosstodloch
Crofts of Dipple
Fochabers
Braes of
MILL
Whiterow
Sueno's Stone
Falconer
Muir of Miltonduff
Longmorn
Clackmarras
North East 250
Dipple
Ordiequish
264
WHITEASH HILL
Forres
Pluscarden
Barnhill
Thomshill
Orbliston
A96
250
THIEF'S HILL
Forgie
River Findhorn
Rafford
Califer
Fogwatt
Millbuies
Inchberry
B9103
B9015
Sound Muir
Aultn Forg
Dallas Dhu Distillery
B9010
Shougle
13
262
FINDLAY'S SEAT
Garbity
Cairnty
Upper Mulben
Rumb
River Lossie
Kellas
Glen of Rothes
A941
Newlands of Dundurcas
Auchroisk
B9103
Mulben
Branchill
NJ
355
PIKEY HILL
Crofts
250
B9010
Dallas
365
CAIRN UISH
Glen Grant
Rothes
Speyside Way
Deanshaugh
Tauchers
Rosar
371
MILL BUIE
Logie
Glen Lossie
400
CARN NA CAILLEICHE
369
HUNT HILL
471
BEN AIGAN
Arndilly House
A95
338
HILL OF TOW
Dunphail
Dandaleith
372
KNOCKAN
B9014
Keith & Dufftown Railway
Glenerney
Maggieknockater
Archiestown
B9102
Craigellachie
B9115
A940
River Dixie
Upper Knockando
Cardhu
Ringorm
Cooperage
Drummuir
522
CARN KITTY
Dava Way
Knockando
Speyview
Charlestown of Aberlour
Glenfiddich
158
543
LARIG HILL
515
ROY'S HILL
Carron
Speyside Way
Glenallachie
B9014
Dava
Snow gates
548
CARN NA LOINE
B9102
Daugh of Kinermony
Milltown of Edinvillie
Dufftown
Balvenie Castle
Milltown of Auchindoun
Dava Moor
Blacksboat
Pitchroy
Marypark
A95
Glenfarclas
Kirktown of Mortlach
A941
Cragganmore
Ballindalloch
Bridge of Avon
Auchindoun Castle
Hau of GI
Lettoch
B9008
840
BEN RINNES
Achnastank
503
CARN CHROM
A947
A95
Advie
North East 250
Glen Rinnes
Glen Fiddich
Cameroy
Snow gates
Delliefure
Mains of Dalvey
Drumin
B9009
River Fiddich
Bridgend
Grantown-on-Spey
Cromdale
B9136
1595
Glenlivet
149
766
CORRYHABBIE HILL
571
ROUND HILL
Cabrach
Speybridge
Craggan
Hills of Cromdale
Glenlivet
Auchbreck
Tomnavoulin
Shenval
Aldivalloch
Aldunie
STRATH SPEY
River Spey
River Avon
Glen Rinnes

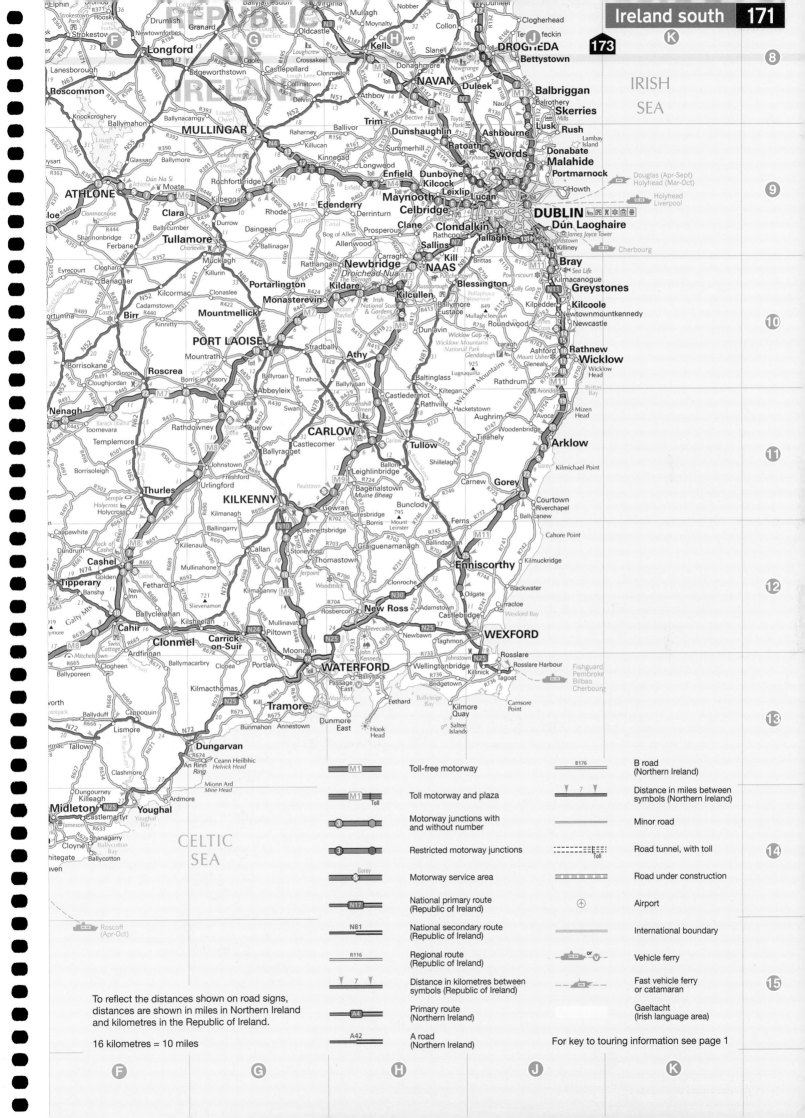

IRISH
SEA

CELTIC
SEA

M1	Toll-free motorway	B176 · B road (Northern Ireland)
M1 Toll	Toll motorway and plaza	▽ 7 ▽ · Distance in miles between symbols (Northern Ireland)
3	Motorway junctions with and without number	Minor road
3	Restricted motorway junctions	Road tunnel, with toll · Toll
S	Motorway service area	Road under construction
N17	National primary route (Republic of Ireland)	⊕ Airport
N81	National secondary route (Republic of Ireland)	International boundary
R116	Regional route (Republic of Ireland)	or V · Vehicle ferry
▽ 7 ▽	Distance in kilometres between symbols (Republic of Ireland)	Fast vehicle ferry or catamaran
A4	Primary route (Northern Ireland)	Gaeltacht (Irish language area)
A42	A road (Northern Ireland)	For key to touring information see page 1

To reflect the distances shown on road signs, distances are shown in miles in Northern Ireland and kilometres in the Republic of Ireland.

16 kilometres = 10 miles

Ireland index

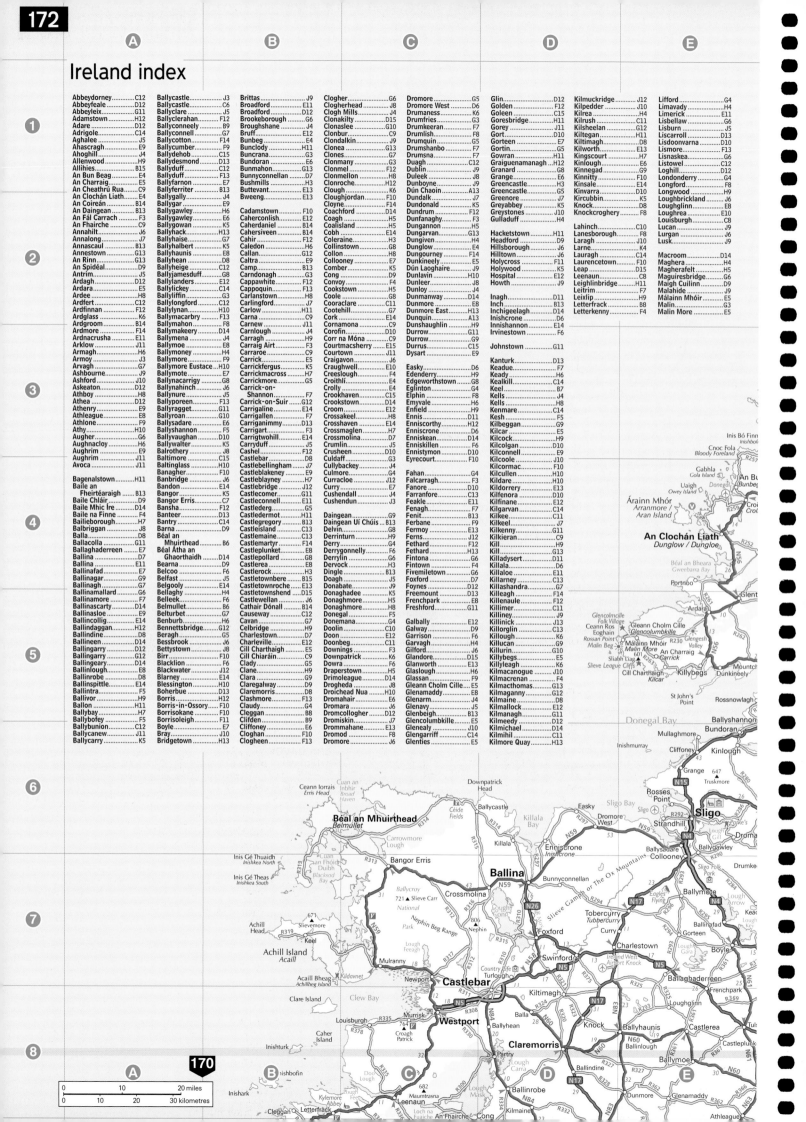

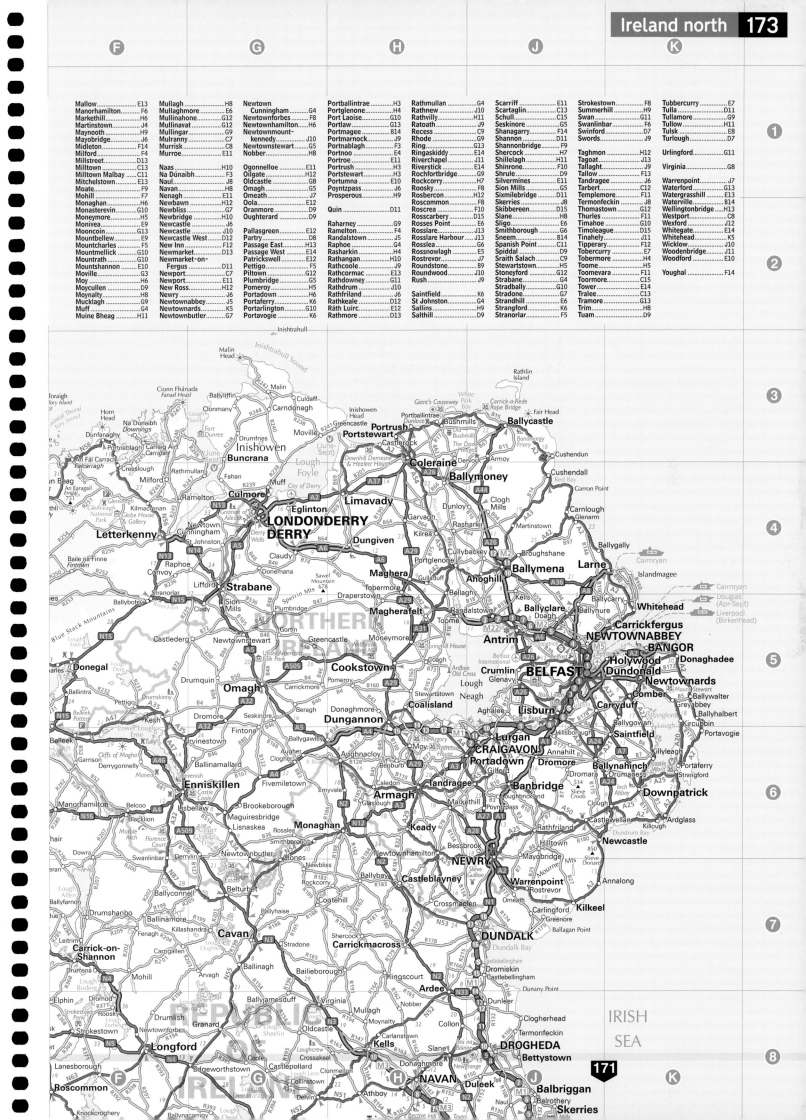

171

For Central London see pages 238–247

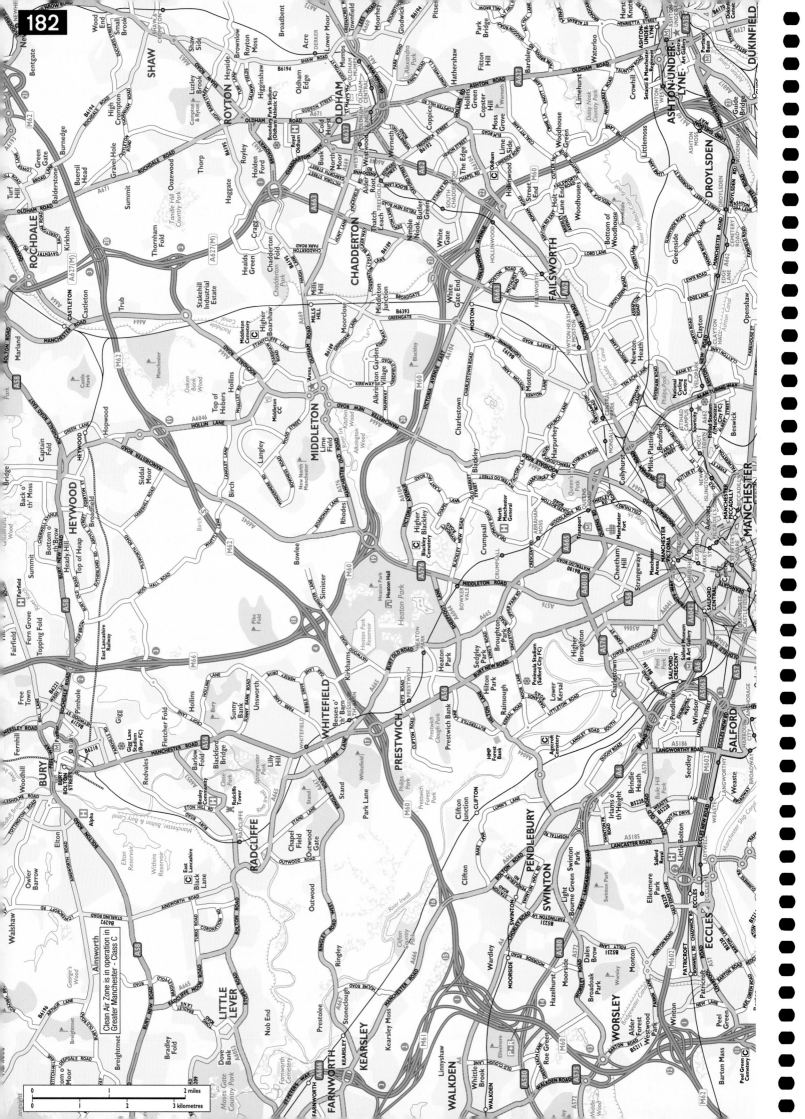

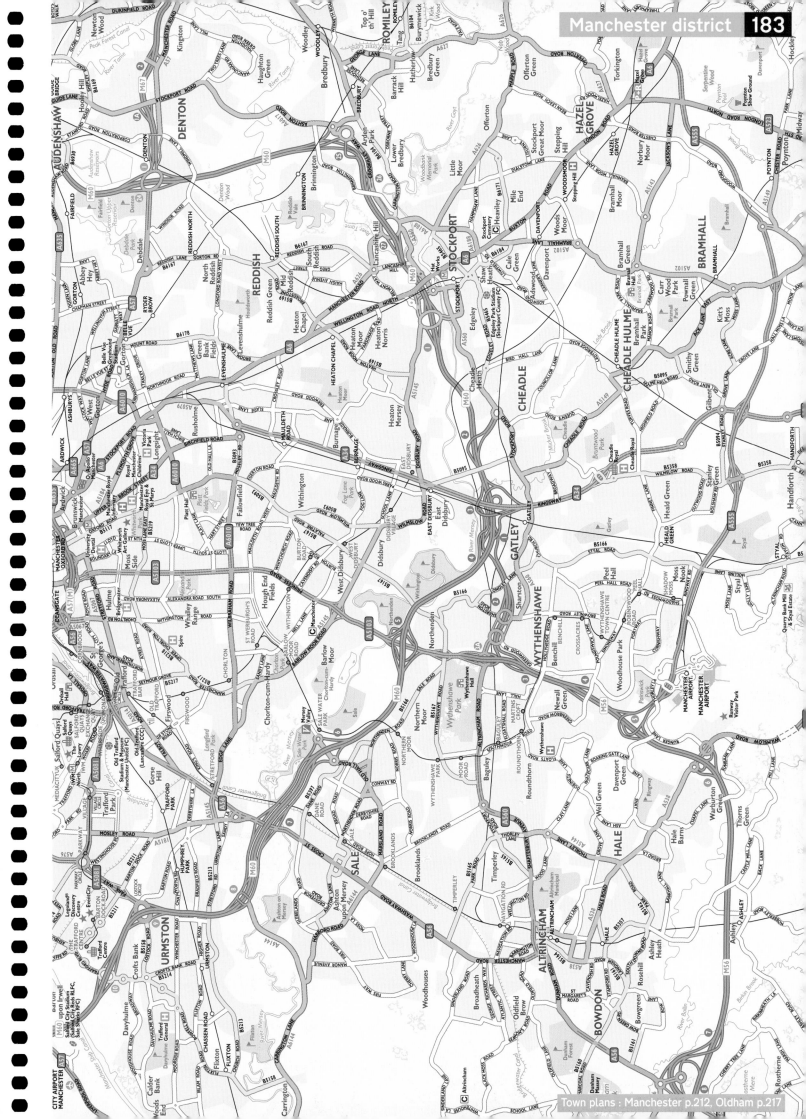

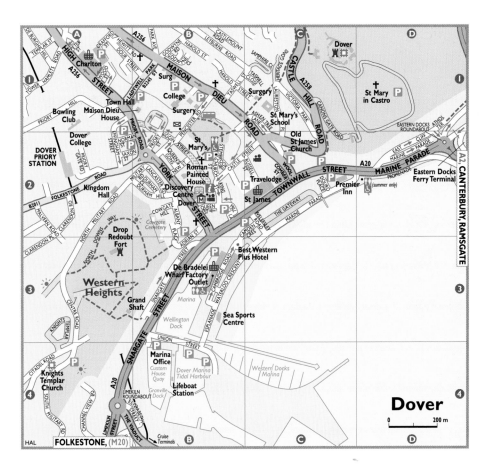

Dover

Dover is found on atlas page **27 P3**

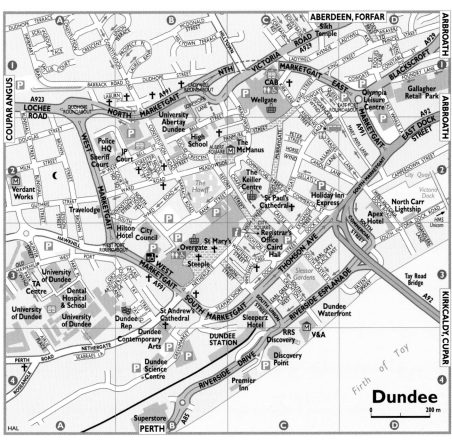

Dundee

Dundee is found on atlas page **142 G11**

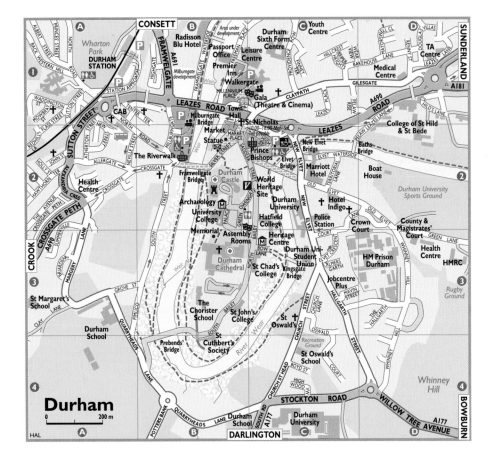

Durham

Durham

Durham is found on atlas page **103 Q2**

Eastbourne

Eastbourne is found on atlas page **25 P11**

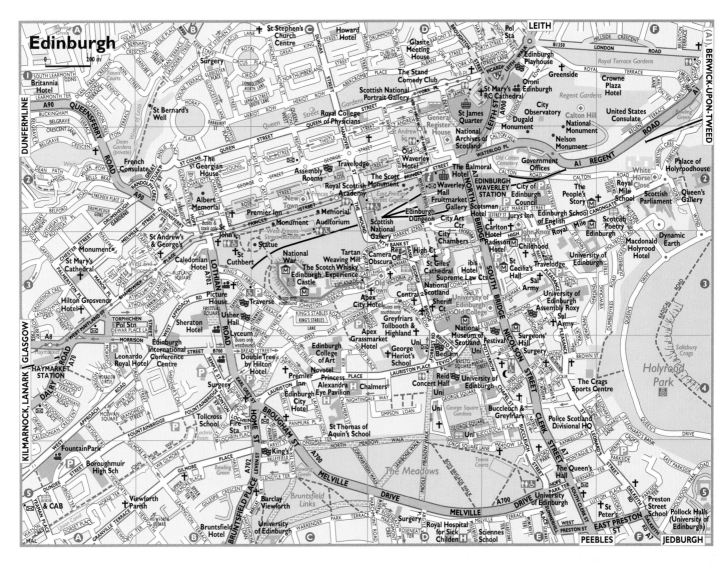

Edinburgh

Edinburgh is found on atlas page **127 P3**

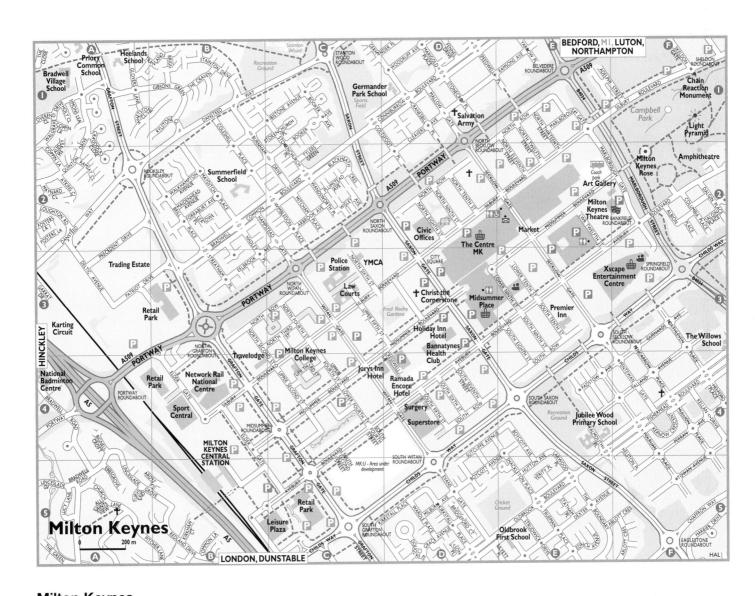

Milton Keynes

Milton Keynes is found on atlas page **49 N7**

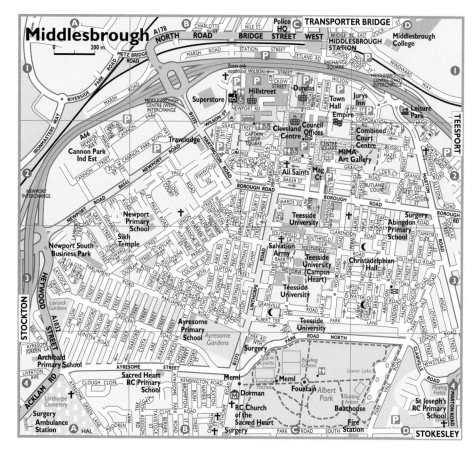

Middlesbrough

Middlesbrough is found on atlas page **104 E7**

Acklam Road	A4	Heywood Street	A3
Acton Street	C3	Ironmasters Way	A2
Aire Street	B4	Kensington Road	B4
Albert Road	C2	Kildare Street	A4
Amber Street	C2	Laurel Street	D3
Athol Street	B3	Lees Road	A2
Aubrey Street	D3	Linthorpe Road	B4
Ayresome Park Road	B4	Longford Street	A4
Ayresome Street	A4	Lorne Street	A3
Borough Road	C2	Lothian Road	D3
Bretnall Street	B2	Marsh Street	A2
Bridge Street East	C1	Marton Road	D2
Bridge Street West	C1	Melrose Street	D2
Bush Street	B4	Metz Bridge Road	A1
Cadogen Street	B3	Myrtle Street	D3
Camden Street	D2	Newlands Road	D3
Cannon Park Road	A2	Newport Road	A2
Cannon Park Way	A2	Palm Street	D3
Cannon Street	A2	Park Lane	C3
Carlow Street	A3	Park Road North	C4
Centre Square	C2	Park Vale Road	D4
Clairville Road	D4	Parliament Road	A3
Clarendon Road	C3	Pearl Street	C2
Clifton Street	B3	Pelham Street	C3
Corporation Road	D1	Portman Street	B3
Costa Street	B4	Princes Road	B3
Craven Street	B3	Riverside Park Road	A1
Crescent Road	A3	Ruby Street	C2
Croydon Road	D3	Russell Street	D2
Derwent Street	A2	St Pauls Road	B2
Diamond Road	B3	Southfield Road	C3
Egmont Road	D4	Station Street	C1
Emily Street	C2	Stowe Street	B3
Errol Street	D3	Tavistock Street	B4
Essex Street	A4	Tennyson Street	B3
Fairbridge Street	C2	Union Street	A3
Falmouth Street	D3	Victoria Road	C3
Finsbury Street	B3	Victoria Street	A3
Fleetham Street	B2	Warren Street	B2
Garnet Street	B2	Waterloo Road	D3
Glebe Road	B3	Waverley Street	B3
Grange Road	B2	Wembley Street	A3
Grange Road	D2	Wilson Street	B2
Granville Road	C3	Wilton Street	C3
Gresham Road	B3	Windsor Street	B2
Harewood Street	B3	Woodlands Road	C3
Harford Street	B4	Worcester Street	B4
Hartington Road	B2	Zetland Road	C1

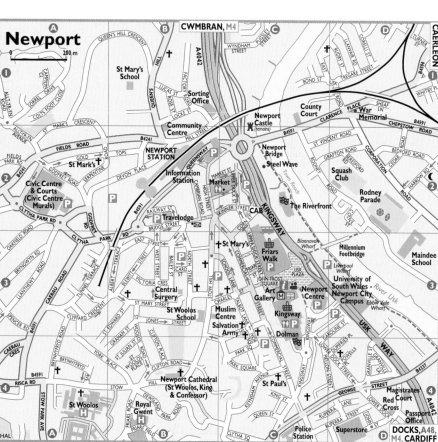

Newport

Newport is found on atlas page **31 K7**

Albert Terrace	B3	Jones Street	B3
Allt-Yr-Yn Avenue	A2	Keynsham Avenue	C4
Bailey Street	B3	King Street	C4
Bedford Road	D2	Kingsway	C2
Blewitt Street	B3	Kingsway	C4
Bond Street	C1	Llanthewy Road	A3
Bridge Street	B2	Locke Street	B1
Bryngwyn Road	A3	Lower Dock Street	C4
Brynhyfryd Avenue	A4	Lucas Street	B1
Brynhyfryd Road	A4	Market Street	B2
Caerau Crescent	A4	Mellon Street	C4
Caerau Road	A3	Mill Street	B2
Cambrian Road	B2	North Street	B3
Caroline Street	D3	Oakfield Road	A3
Cedar Road	D2	Park Square	C4
Charles Street	C3	Queen's Hill	B1
Chepstow Road	D1	Queen's Hill Crescent	A1
Clarence Place	C1	Queen Street	C4
Clifton Place	B4	Queensway	B2
Clifton Road	B4	Risca Road	A4
Clyffard Crescent	A3	Rodney Road	C2
Clytha Park Road	A2	Rudry Street	D1
Clytha Square	C4	Ruperra Lane	C4
Colts Foot Close	A1	Ruperra Street	D4
Commercial Street	C3	St Edward Street	B3
Corelli Street	D1	St Julian Street	B4
Corn Street	C2	St Mark's Crescent	A2
Corporation Road	D2	St Mary Street	B3
Devon Place	B2	St Vincent Road	C2
Dewsland Park Road	B4	St Woolos Road	B3
Dumfries Place	D4	School Lane	C3
East Street	B3	Serpentine Road	A2
East Usk Road	C1	Skinner Street	C2
Factory Road	B1	Sorrel Drive	A1
Fields Road	A2	Spencer Road	A3
Friars Field	B4	Stow Hill	B3
Friars Road	B4	Stow Hill	B4
Friar Street	C3	Stow Park Avenue	A4
George Street	D4	Talbot Lane	C3
Godfrey Road	A2	Tregare Street	D1
Gold Tops	A2	Tunnel Terrace	A3
Grafton Road	C2	Upper Dock Street	C2
Granville Lane	D4	Upper Dock Street	C3
Granville Street	D4	Usk Way	D3
High Street	B2	Victoria Crescent	A3
Hill Street	C3	West Street	B3
John Frost Square	C3	Wyndham Stret	C1
John Street	D4	York Place	A4

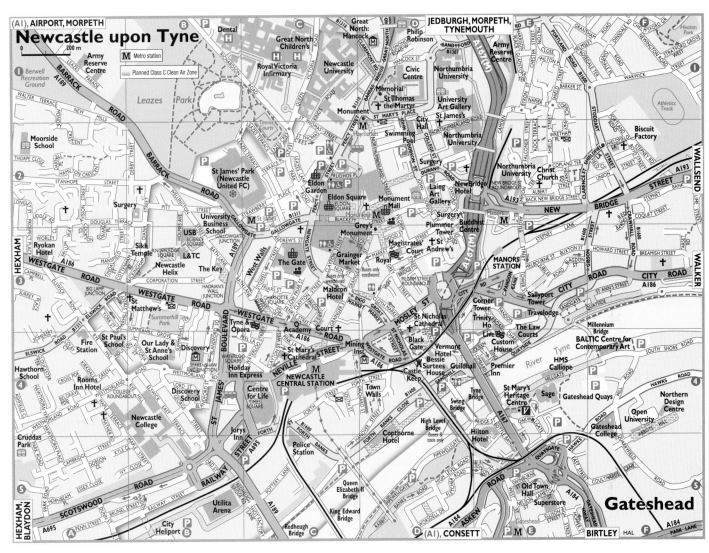

Newcastle upon Tyne

Newcastle upon Tyne is found on atlas page **113 K8**

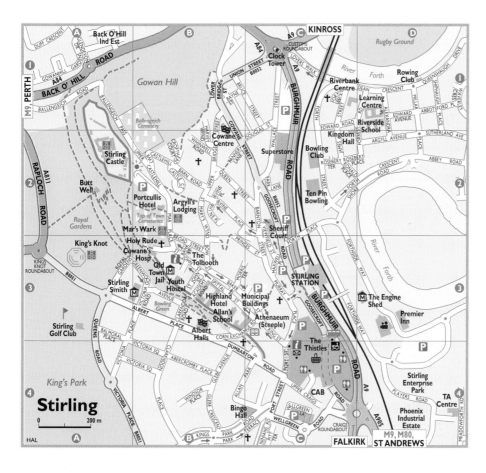

Stirling

Stirling

Stirling is found on atlas page **133 M9**

Stockton-on-Tees

Stockton-on-Tees is found on atlas page **104 D7**

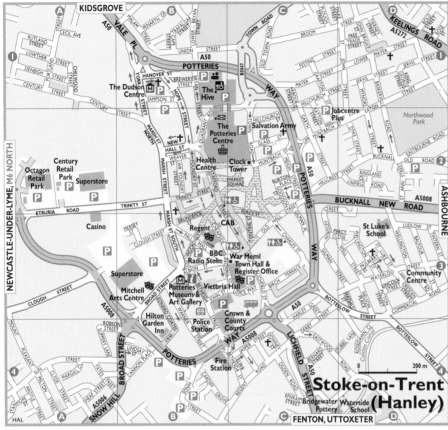

Stoke-on-Trent (Hanley)

Stoke-on-Trent (Hanley) is found on atlas page **70 F5**

Albion Street......................B3	Linfield Road........................D2
Bagnall Street.....................B3	Lower Mayer Street..............D1
Balfour Street.....................D3	Lowther Street......................A1
Baskerville Road..................D1	Ludlow Street.......................D3
Bathesda Street...................B4	Malam Street........................B1
Bernard Street C4	Marsh Street.........................B2
Bethesda Street...................B3	Marsh Street North...............B2
Birch Terrace......................C3	Marsh Street South...............B3
Botteslow Street..................C3	Mayer Street.........................C1
Broad Street........................B4	Mersey Street.......................B3
Broom Street......................C1	Milton Street........................A4
Brunswick Street.................B3	Mount Pleasant....................A4
Bryan Street........................B1	Mynors Street.......................D1
Bucknall New Road C2	New Hall Street.....................B2
Bucknall Old Road................D2	Ogden Road..........................C4
Cardiff Grove.......................B4	Old Hall Street......................C3
Century Street.....................A1	Old Town Road......................C1
Charles Street......................C3	Pall Mall...............................B3
Cheapside...........................B3	Percy Street..........................C2
Chelwood Street..................A1	Piccadilly..............................B3
Clough Street......................A3	Portland Street......................A1
Clyde Street.........................A4	Potteries Way........................B1
Commercial Road.................D3	Potteries Way........................B4
Denbigh Street.....................A1	Quadrant Road......................B2
Derby Street.........................C4	Regent Road.........................C4
Dyke Street..........................D2	Rutland Street.......................A1
Eastwood Road....................C4	St John Street........................D1
Eaton Street.........................D2	St Luke Street........................D3
Etruria Road.........................A2	Sampson Street......................B1
Foundry Street......................B2	Sheaf Street...........................A4
Garth Street..........................C2	Slippery Lane.........................A4
Gilman Street.......................C3	Snow Hill..............................A4
Goodson Street.....................C2	Stafford Street.......................B2
Grafton Street......................C1	Sun Street.............................A4
Hanover Street......................B1	Tontine Street.......................C3
Harley Street........................C4	Town Road............................C2
Hillchurch............................C2	Trafalgar Street.....................B1
Hillcrest Street......................C2	Trinity Street.........................B2
Hinde Street.........................B4	Union Street..........................B1
Hope Street...........................B1	Upper Hillchurch Street.........C2
Hordley Street.......................C3	Upper Huntbach Street..........C2
Huntbach Street....................C2	Warner Street........................B3
Jasper Street.........................C4	Waterloo Street.....................D3
Jervis Street..........................D1	Well Street............................D3
John Street...........................B3	Wellington Road....................D3
Keelings Road D1	Wellington Street...................D3
Lichfield Street.....................C3	Yates Street...........................A4
Lidice Way C3	York Street............................B1

Stratford-upon-Avon

Stratford-upon-Avon is found on atlas page **47 P3**

Albany Road.........................A3	New Broad Street...................B4
Alcester Road.......................A2	New Street............................B4
Arden Street B2	Old Red Lion Court C2
Avenue Road........................C1	Old Town..............................C4
Bancroft Place......................C2	Orchard Way.........................A4
Birmingham Road B1	Payton Street........................C2
Brewery Street......................B1	Percy Street...........................C1
Bridge Foot..........................D2	Rother Street.........................B3
Bridge Street........................C2	Rowley Crescent D1
Bridgeway............................D2	Ryland Street.........................B4
Broad Street.........................B4	St Andrew's Crescent.............A3
Brookvale Road.....................A4	St Gregory's Road..................C1
Brunel Way...........................A2	St Martin's Close...................A3
Bull Street............................B4	Sanctus Drive........................B4
Cedar Close..........................D1	Sanctus Road........................A4
Chapel Lane.........................C3	Sanctus Street.......................B4
Chapel Street.......................C3	Sandfield Road......................A4
Cherry Orchard.....................A4	Scholars Lane........................B3
Cherry Street........................B4	Seven Meadows Road............A4
Chestnut Walk......................B3	Shakespeare Street................B1
Church Street........................B3	Sheep Street..........................C3
Clopton Bridge.....................D3	Shipston Road.......................D4
Clopton Road.......................B1	Shottery Road........................A3
College Lane.........................B4	Shrieves Walk.......................C3
College Mews.......................B4	Southern Lane.......................C3
College Street.......................B4	Swan's Nest...........................D3
Ely Gardens.........................B3	The Willows..........................A3
Ely Street.............................B3	Tiddington Road D3
Evesham Place......................B3	Town Square.........................B2
Evesham Road......................A4	Tramway Bridge D3
Garrick Way.........................A4	Tyler Street...........................C2
Great William Street.............C1	Union Street..........................C2
Greenhill Street....................B2	Warwick Court......................C1
Grove Road..........................B3	Warwick Crescent.................D1
Guild Street..........................C2	Warwick Road.......................C2
Henley Street........................C2	Waterside..............................C3
High Street...........................C3	Welcombe Road....................D1
Holtom Street.......................B4	Wellesbourne Grove..............B2
John Street...........................C2	Western Road........................B1
Kendall Avenue....................B1	West Street...........................B4
Lock Close............................C2	Willows Drive North..............A2
Maidenhead Road................C1	Windsor Street.......................B2
Mansell Street.......................B2	Wood Street..........................B2
Mayfield Avenue...................C1	
Meer Street..........................B2	
Mill Lane..............................C4	
Mulberry Street....................C1	
Narrow Lane B4	

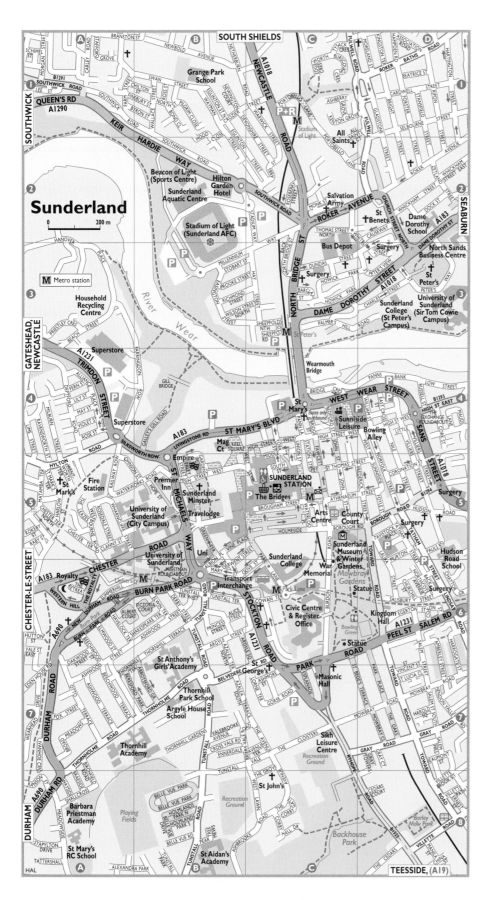

Sunderland

Sunderland is found on atlas page **113 N9**

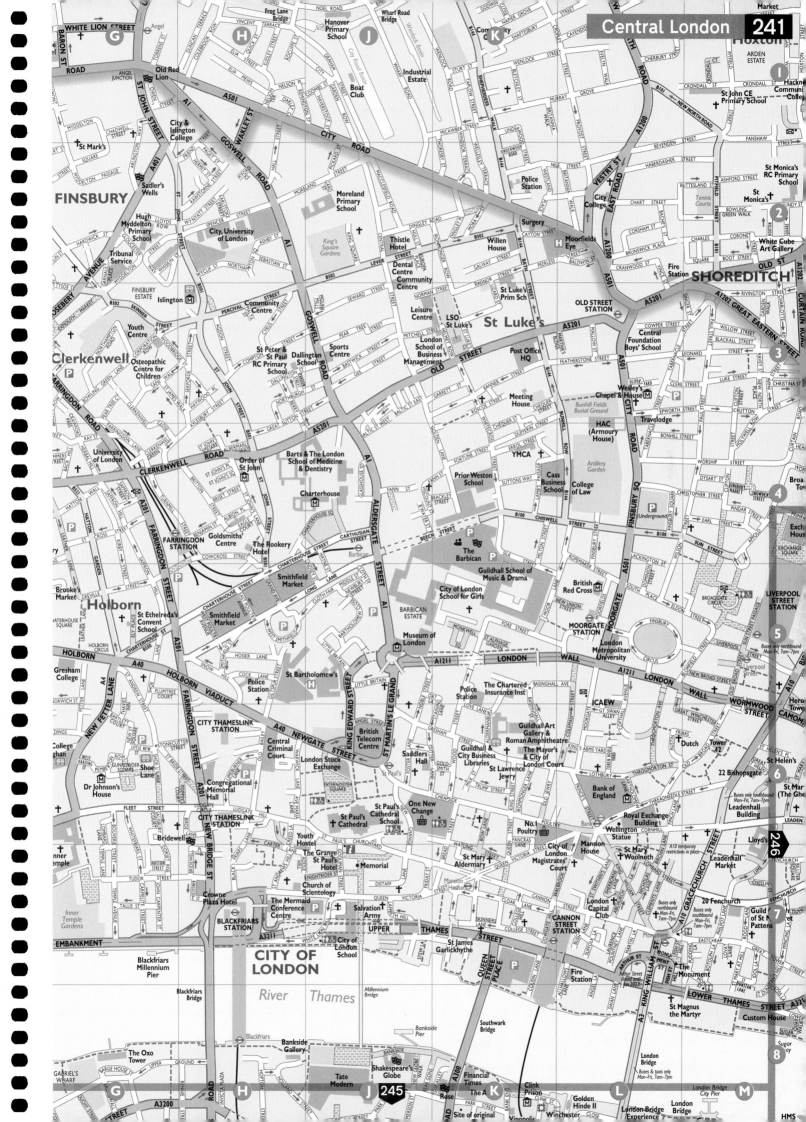

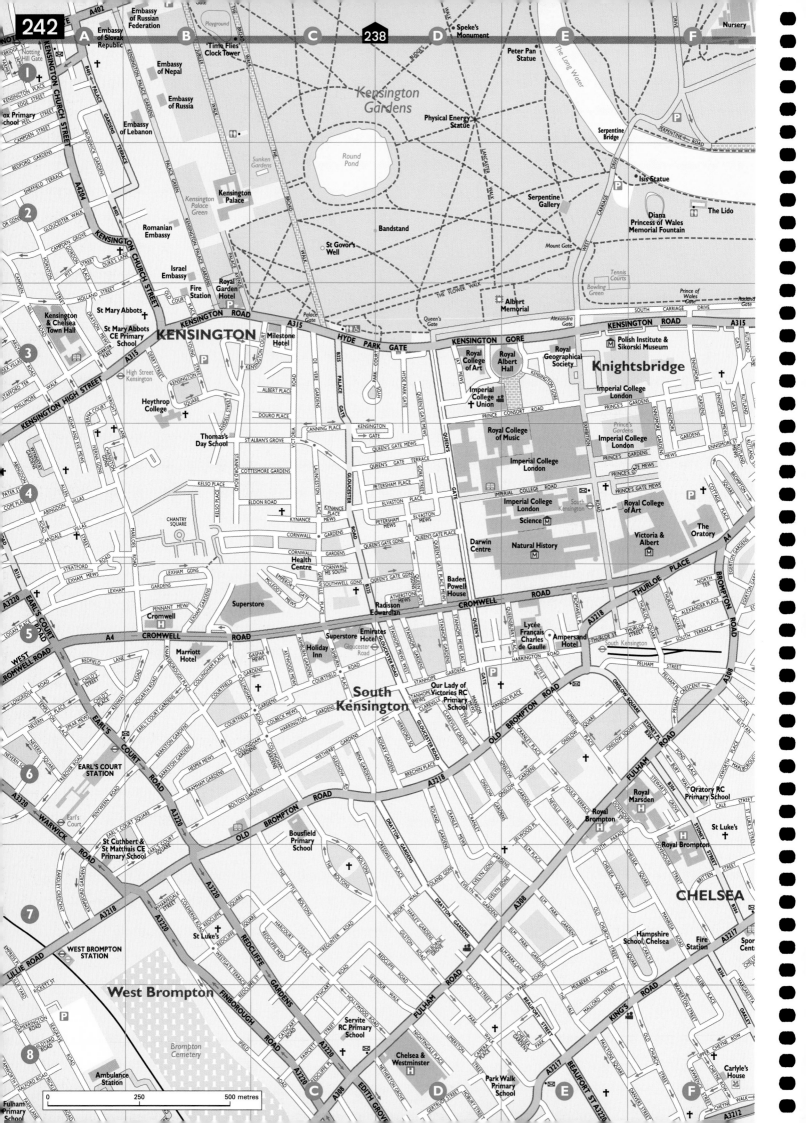

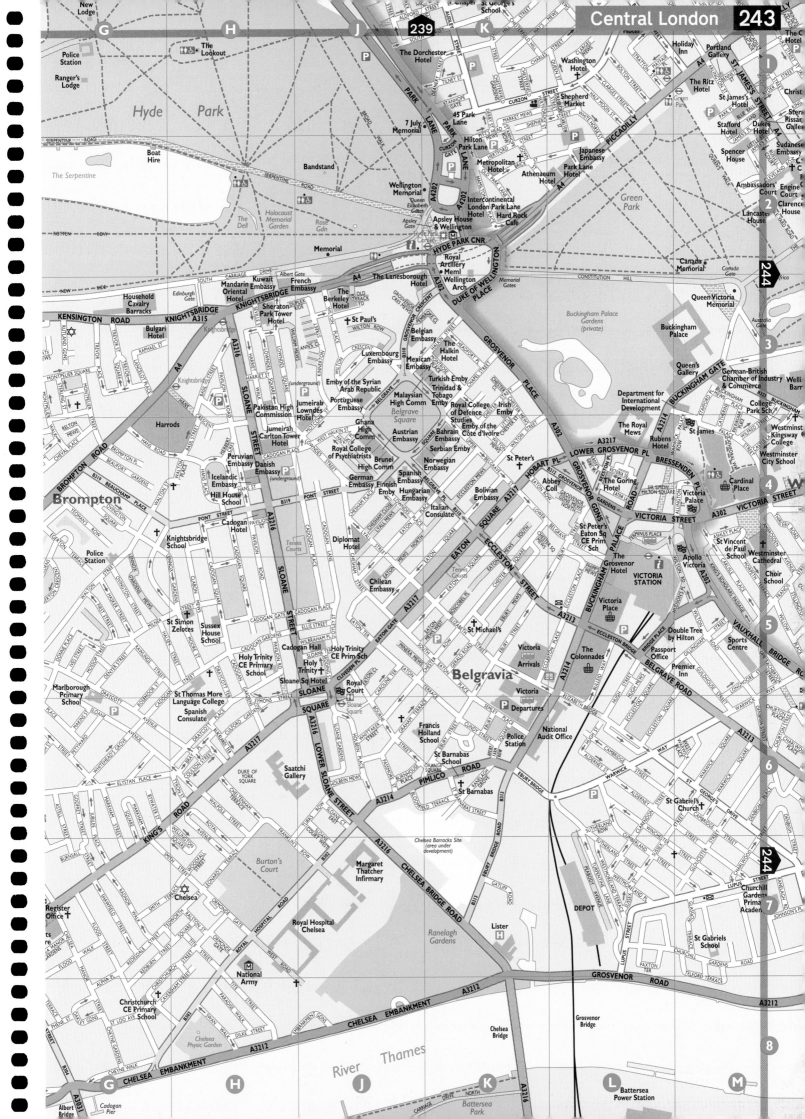

Hewelsfield – Honington 275

Hewelsfield Gloucs 31 Q4
Hewenden C Brad 90 D3
Hewish N Som 19 M2
Hewish Somset 11 J3
Hewood Dorset 10 H4
Hexham Nthumb 112 D8
Hextable Kent 37 M6
Hexthorpe Donc 91 P10
Hexton Herts 50 D4
Hexworthy Cnwll 5 P5
Hexworthy Devon 6 H4
Hey Lancs 89 P2
Heybridge Essex 51 P11
Heybridge Essex 52 E10
Heybridge Basin Essex 52 E10
Heybrook Bay Devon 6 D9
Heydon Cambs 51 K3
Heydon Norfk 76 G6
Heydour Lincs 73 Q3
Hey Houses Lancs 88 C5
Heylipoll Ag & B 136 B7
Heylor Shet 169 p5
Heyrod Tamesd 83 L5
Heysham Lancs 95 J8
Heyshaw N York 97 J8
Heyshott W Susx 23 N11
Heyside Oldham 89 Q9
Heytesbury Wilts 20 H6
Heythrop Oxon 48 C9
Heywood Rochdl 89 P8
Heywood Wilts 20 G4
Hibaldstow N Linc 92 G10
Hickleton Donc 91 M9
Hickling Norfk 77 N7
Hickling Notts 72 H5
Hickling Green Norfk 77 N7
Hickling Heath Norfk 77 N7
Hickling Pastures Notts 72 H5
Hickmans Green Kent 39 J10
Hicks Forstal Kent 39 L9
Hickstead W Susx 24 G6
Hidcote Bartrim Gloucs 47 N6
Hidcote Boyce Gloucs 47 N6
High Ackworth Wakefd 91 L7
Higham Barns 91 J9
Higham Derbys 84 E9
Higham Kent 37 P11
Higham Kent 38 B7
Higham Lancs 89 N3
Higham Suffk 52 H4
Higham Suffk 63 M7
Higham Dykes Nthumb 112 H5
Higham Ferrers Nhants 61 L7
Higham Gobion C Beds 50 D4
Higham Hill Gt Lon 37 J2
Higham on the Hill Leics 72 B11
Highampton Devon 8 C4
Highams Park Gt Lon 37 J2
High Angerton Nthumb 112 G3
High Ardwell D & G 106 E8
High Auldgirth D & G 109 K3
High Bankhill Cumb 101 Q2
High Barnet Gt Lon 50 G11
High Beach Essex 51 K11
High Bentham N York 95 P7
High Bewaldeth Cumb 100 H4
High Bickington Devon 17 L7
High Biggins Cumb 95 N5
High Birkwith N York 96 B5
High Blantyre S Lans 126 B6
High Bonnybridge Falk 126 E2
High Borrans Cumb 101 M10
High Bradley N York 96 F11
High Bray Devon 17 M5
Highbridge Hants 22 E10
Highbridge Somset 19 K5
Highbrook W Susx 25 J4
High Brooms Kent 25 N2
High Bullen Devon 17 J7
Highburton Kirk 90 F8
Highbury Gt Lon 36 H3
Highbury Somset 20 C5
High Buston Nthumb 119 P9
High Callerton Nthumb 113 J6
High Casterton Cumb 95 N5
High Catton E R Yk 98 E10
Highclere Hants 22 D3
Highcliffe BCP 13 M6
High Close Dur 103 N7
High Cogges Oxon 34 C3
High Common Norfk 76 D10
High Coniscliffe Darltn 103 P7
High Crosby Cumb 111 J9
High Cross Cnwll 3 J8
High Cross E Ayrs 125 L8
High Cross Hants 23 K9
High Cross Herts 51 J7
Highcross Lancs 88 C3
High Cross W Susx 24 F7
High Cross Warwks 59 K11
High Drummore D & G 106 F10
High Dubmire Sundld 113 M11
High Easter Essex 51 P8
High Eggborough N York 91 P6
High Ellington N York 97 J4
Higher Alham Somset 20 C6
Higher Ansty Dorset 12 C4
Higher Ballam Lancs 88 D4
Higher Bartle Lancs 88 G4
Higher Berry End C Beds 49 Q8
Higher Bockhampton Dorset 12 B6
Higher Brixham Torbay 7 N8
Higher Burrowton Devon 9 P5
Higher Burwardsley Ches W 69 P3
High Ercall Wrekin 69 Q11
Higher Chillington Somset 10 H2
Higher Clovelly Devon 16 E7
Highercombe Somset 18 B8
Higher Coombe Dorset 11 L6
Higher Disley Ches E 83 L8
Higher Folds Wigan 82 E4
Higherford Lancs 89 P2
Higher Gabwell Devon 7 N5
Higher Halstock Leigh Dorset 11 L3
Higher Harpers Lancs 89 N3
Higher Heysham Lancs 95 J8
Higher Hurdsfield Ches E 83 K10
Higher Irlam Salfd 82 F5
Higher Kingcombe Dorset 11 L5
Higher Kinnerton Flints 69 K2
Higher Marston Ches W 82 E9
Higher Muddiford Devon 17 K4
Higher Nyland Dorset 20 D10
Higher Ogden Rochdl 90 B8
Higher Pentire Cnwll 2 H8
Higher Penwortham Lancs 88 G5
Higher Prestacott Devon 5 P2
Higher Studfold N York 96 B6
Higher Town Cnwll 3 L5
Higher Town Cnwll 4 G9
Higher Town IoS 2 c1
Higher Tregantle Cnwll 5 Q11
Higher Walton Lancs 88 H5
Higher Walton Warrtn 82 C7
Higher Wambrook Somset 10 F3
Higher Waterston Dorset 11 Q5
Higher Whatcombe Dorset 12 D4
Higher Wheelton Lancs 89 J6
Higher Whitley Ches W 82 D8
Higher Wincham Ches W 82 E9
Higher Wraxhall Dorset 11 M4
Higher Wych Ches W 69 N6
High Etherley Dur 103 N5
High Ferry Lincs 87 L11
Highfield E R Yk 92 B3
Highfield Gatesd 112 H9
Highfield N Ayrs 125 J7
Highfields Donc 91 N9
Highfields Caldecote Cambs 62 E9
High Flats Kirk 90 G9
High Garrett Essex 52 C6
Highgate E Susx 25 K4
Highgate Gt Lon 36 G3
Highgate Kent 26 C5
High Grange Dur 103 N4
High Grantley N York 97 K7
High Green Cumb 101 M10
High Green Kirk 90 G8
High Green Norfk 64 H4
High Green Norfk 76 G10
High Green Sheff 91 J11
High Green Shrops 57 N8
High Green Suffk 64 B9
High Green Worcs 46 G5
Highgreen Manor Nthumb 112 B2
High Halden Kent 26 E4
High Halstow Medway 38 C6
High Ham Somset 19 M8
High Harrington Cumb 100 D5
High Harrogate N York 97 M9
High Haswell Dur 104 C2
High Hatton Shrops 69 R10
High Hauxley Nthumb 119 Q10
High Hawsker N York 105 P9
High Hesket Cumb 101 N2
High Hoyland Barns 90 H9
High Hunsley E R Yk 92 G3
High Hurstwood E Susx 25 L5
High Hutton N York 98 F7
High Ireby Cumb 100 H3
High Kelling Norfk 76 G3
High Kilburn N York 97 R5
High Killerby N York 99 M4
High Knipe Cumb 101 P7
High Lands Dur 103 M5
Highlane Ches E 83 J11
Highlane Derbys 84 F4
High Lane Stockp 83 L7
High Lanes Cnwll 2 F6
High Laver Essex 51 M9
Highlaws Cumb 109 P11
Highleadon Gloucs 46 E10
High Legh Ches E 82 F8
Highleigh W Susx 15 M7
High Leven S on T 104 E8
Highley Shrops 57 N8
High Littleton BaNES 20 B3
High Lorton Cumb 100 G5
High Marishes N York 98 G5
High Marnham Notts 85 P6
High Melton Donc 91 N10
High Mickley Nthumb 112 G8
Highmoor Cumb 110 E11
Highmoor Oxon 35 K8
Highmoor Cross Oxon 35 K8
Highmoor Hill Mons 31 N7
High Moorsley Sundld 113 M11
Highnam Gloucs 46 E10
High Newport Sundld 113 N10
High Newton Cumb 95 J4
High Newton-by-the-Sea Nthumb 119 P5
High Nibthwaite Cumb 94 F3
High Offley Staffs 70 D9
High Ongar Essex 51 N10
High Onn Staffs 70 E11
High Park Corner Essex 52 H7
High Pennyvenie E Ayrs 115 J6
High Pittington Dur 104 B2
High Post Wilts 21 N7
Highridge N Som 31 Q11
High Roding Essex 51 P7
High Row Cumb 101 L3
High Row Cumb 101 L6
High Salter Lancs 95 N8
High Salvington W Susx 24 D9
High Scales Cumb 110 C11
High Seaton Cumb 100 D4
High Shaw N York 96 C2
High Side Cumb 100 H4
High Spen Gatesd 112 H9
Highstead Kent 39 M8
Highsted Kent 38 F9
High Stoop Dur 103 M2
High Street Cnwll 3 P3
High Street Kent 26 B5
Highstreet Kent 39 J9
High Street Suffk 65 N10
High Street Suffk 65 N7
Highstreet Green Essex 52 C5
Highstreet Green Surrey 23 Q7
Hightae D & G 109 N5
Highter's Heath Birm 58 G9
High Throston Hartpl 104 E4
Hightown Ches E 70 F2
Hightown Hants 13 L4
Hightown Sefton 81 L4
High Town Staffs 58 E2
Hightown Green Suffk 64 D10
High Toynton Lincs 87 J7
High Trewhitt Nthumb 119 K9
High Urpeth Dur 113 K10
High Valleyfield Fife 134 C10
High Warden Nthumb 112 D7
Highway Herefs 45 P5
Highway Wilts 33 K10
Highweek Devon 7 L4
High Westwood Dur 112 H9
Highwood Essex 51 P10
Highwood Staffs 71 K8
Highwood W Susx 24 E4
Highwood Hill Gt Lon 36 F2
High Woolaston Gloucs 31 Q5
High Worsall N York 104 C9
Highworth Swindn 33 P6
High Wray Cumb 101 L11
High Wych Herts 51 L8
High Wycombe Bucks 35 N6
Hilborough Norfk 75 R10
Hilcote Derbys 84 G9
Hilcott Wilts 21 M3
Hildenborough Kent 37 N11
Hilden Park Kent 37 N11
Hildersham Cambs 62 H11
Hilderstone Staffs 70 H8
Hilderthorpe E R Yk 99 P7
Hilfield Dorset 11 N3
Hilgay Norfk 75 M11
Hill S Glos 32 B5
Hill Warwks 59 Q11
Hillam N York 91 N5
Hillbeck Cumb 102 E7
Hillborough Kent 39 M8
Hill Brow Hants 23 L9
Hillbutts Dorset 12 G4
Hill Chorlton Staffs 70 D7
Hillclifflane Derbys 71 P5
Hill Common Norfk 77 N7
Hill Common Somset 18 F9
Hill Deverill Wilts 20 G6
Hilldyke Lincs 87 K11
Hill End Dur 103 K3
Hill End Fife 134 C8
Hillend Fife 134 E11
Hill End Gloucs 46 H7
Hillend Mdloth 127 P4
Hillend N Lans 126 E4
Hillend Swans 28 D6
Hillersland Gloucs 31 Q2
Hillerton Devon 8 H5
Hillesden Bucks 49 J9
Hillesley Gloucs 32 E7
Hillfarrance Somset 18 G10
Hill Green Kent 38 D9
Hillgrove W Susx 23 P9
Hillhampton Herefs 46 A5
Hillhead Abers 158 E10
Hillhead Devon 7 N8
Hill Head Hants 14 F6
Hillhead S Lans 116 D2
Hillhead of Cocklaw Abers 159 Q9
Hilliard's Cross Staffs 59 J2
Hilliclay Highld 167 L4
Hillingdon Gt Lon 36 C4
Hillington C Glas 125 N5
Hillington Norfk 75 P5
Hillis Corner IoW 14 E8
Hillmorton Warwks 60 B6
Hillock Vale Lancs 89 M5
Hill of Beath Fife 134 F9
Hill of Fearn Highld 163 J11
Hillowton D & G 108 G8
Hillpool Worcs 58 C9
Hillpound Hants 22 G11
Hill Ridware Staffs 71 K11
Hillside Abers 151 N8
Hillside Angus 143 N5
Hillside Devon 7 J6
Hill Side Kirk 90 F7
Hill Side Worcs 46 E2
Hills Town Derbys 84 G7
Hillstreet Hants 22 B11
Hillswick Shet 169 p6
Hill Top Dur 103 J6
Hill Top Hants 14 D6
Hill Top Kirk 90 D8
Hill Top Rothm 84 E2
Hill Top Sandw 58 E6
Hill Top Wakefd 91 J7
Hillwell Shet 169 q12
Hilmarton Wilts 33 K9
Hilperton Wilts 20 G3
Hilperton Marsh Wilts 20 G3
Hilsea C Port 15 J6
Hilston E R Yk 93 N4
Hiltingbury Hants 22 D10
Hilton Border 129 M9
Hilton Cambs 62 C7
Hilton Cumb 102 D6
Hilton Derbys 71 N8
Hilton Dorset 12 C4
Hilton Dur 103 N6
Hilton S on T 104 E8
Hilton Shrops 57 P5
Hilton of Cadboll Highld 156 F2
Hilton Park Services Staffs 58 E4
Himbleton Worcs 46 H3
Himley Staffs 58 C6
Hincaster Cumb 95 L4
Hinchley Wood Surrey 36 E7
Hinckley Leics 59 P6
Hinderclay Suffk 64 E6
Hinderwell N York 105 L7
Hindford Shrops 69 K8
Hindhead Surrey 23 N7
Hindhead Tunnel Surrey 23 N7
Hindle Fold Lancs 89 L4
Hindley Nthumb 112 F9
Hindley Wigan 82 D4
Hindley Green Wigan 82 D4
Hindlip Worcs 46 G3
Hindolveston Norfk 76 E6
Hindon Wilts 20 H8
Hindringham Norfk 76 D4
Hingham Norfk 76 E11
Hinksford Staffs 58 C7
Hinstock Shrops 70 B9
Hintlesham Suffk 53 J3
Hinton Gloucs 32 C4
Hinton Hants 13 M5
Hinton Herefs 45 L7
Hinton Nhants 48 F4
Hinton S Glos 32 D9
Hinton Shrops 56 G3
Hinton Shrops 57 M8
Hinton Admiral Hants 13 M5
Hinton Ampner Hants 22 H9
Hinton Blewett BaNES 19 Q3
Hinton Charterhouse BaNES 20 E3
Hinton Cross Worcs 47 K6
Hinton-in-the-Hedges Nhants 48 G7
Hinton Marsh Hants 22 G9
Hinton Martell Dorset 12 H3
Hinton on the Green Worcs 47 K6
Hinton Parva Swindn 33 P8
Hinton St George Somset 11 J2
Hinton St Mary Dorset 20 E11
Hinton Waldrist Oxon 34 C5
Hints Shrops 57 L10
Hints Staffs 59 J4
Hinwick Bed 61 K8
Hinxhill Kent 26 H3
Hinxton Cambs 62 G11
Hinxworth Herts 50 F2
Hipperholme Calder 90 E5
Hipsburn Nthumb 119 P8
Hipswell N York 103 N11
Hirn Abers 151 J7
Hirnant Powys 68 D10
Hirst Nthumb 113 L3
Hirst Courtney N York 91 Q6
Hirwaen Denbgs 68 F2
Hirwaun Rhondd 30 C3
Hiscott Devon 17 J6
Histon Cambs 62 F8
Hitcham Suffk 64 D11
Hitcham Causeway Suffk 64 D11
Hitcham Street Suffk 64 D11
Hitchin Herts 50 E5
Hither Green Gt Lon 37 J6
Hittisleigh Devon 8 H5
Hive E R Yk 92 D4
Hixon Staffs 71 J9
Hoaden Kent 39 N10
Hoar Cross Staffs 71 L10
Hoarwithy Herefs 45 Q9
Hoath Kent 39 M9
Hoathly Kent 25 Q3
Hobarris Shrops 56 E9
Hobbles Green Suffk 63 M10
Hobbs Cross Essex 51 L11
Hobbs Cross Essex 51 L8
Hobkirk Border 118 A8
Hobland Hall Norfk 77 Q11
Hobsick Notts 84 G11
Hobson Dur 113 J9
Hoby Leics 72 H7
Hoccombe Somset 18 F9
Hockering Norfk 76 F9
Hockerton Notts 85 M9
Hockley Ches E 83 K8
Hockley Covtry 59 L9
Hockley Essex 38 D3
Hockley Staffs 59 K4
Hockley Heath Solhll 59 J10
Hockliffe C Beds 49 Q9
Hockwold cum Wilton Norfk 63 M3
Hockworthy Devon 18 D11
Hoddesdon Herts 51 J9
Hoddlesden Bl w D 89 L6
Hoddom Cross D & G 110 C6
Hoddom Mains D & G 110 C6
Hodgehill Ches E 82 H11
Hodgeston Pembks 41 K11
Hodnet Shrops 69 R9
Hodsock Notts 85 K3
Hodsoll Street Kent 37 P8
Hodson Swindn 33 N8
Hodthorpe Derbys 84 H5
Hoe Hants 22 G11
Hoe Norfk 76 D8
Hoe Benham W Berk 34 D11
Hoe Gate Hants 14 H4
Hoff Cumb 102 C7
Hogben's Hill Kent 38 H10
Hoggards Green Suffk 64 B10
Hoggeston Bucks 49 M10
Hoggrill's End Warwks 59 K6
Hog Hill E Susx 26 E8
Hoghton Lancs 89 J5
Hoghton Bottoms Lancs 89 J5
Hognaston Derbys 71 N4
Hogsthorpe Lincs 87 P6
Holbeach Lincs 74 G6
Holbeach Bank Lincs 74 G5
Holbeach Clough Lincs 74 G5
Holbeach Drove Lincs 74 F8
Holbeach Hurn Lincs 74 G5
Holbeach St Johns Lincs 74 G7
Holbeach St Mark's Lincs 74 G4
Holbeach St Matthew Lincs 74 H4
Holbeck Notts 84 H6
Holbeck Woodhouse Notts 84 H6
Holberrow Green Worcs 47 K3
Holbeton Devon 6 G8
Holborn Gt Lon 36 H4
Holborough Kent 37 Q8
Holbrook Derbys 72 B2
Holbrook Sheff 84 F4
Holbrook Suffk 53 L4
Holbrook Moor Derbys 84 E11
Holbrooks Covtry 59 M8
Holburn Nthumb 119 K3
Holbury Hants 14 D6
Holcombe Devon 7 P4
Holcombe Somset 20 C5
Holcombe Rogus Devon 18 E11
Holcot Nhants 60 G7
Holden Lancs 96 A11
Holdenby Nhants 60 E7
Holden Gate Calder 89 P6
Holder's Green Essex 51 P5
Holdgate Shrops 57 K7
Holdingham Lincs 86 E11
Holditch Dorset 10 G4
Holdsworth Calder 90 D5
Holehouse Derbys 83 M6
Hole-in-the-Wall Herefs 46 B9
Holemoor Devon 16 G10
Hole Street W Susx 24 D8
Holford Somset 18 G6
Holgate C York 98 B10
Holker Cumb 94 H5
Holkham Norfk 76 B3
Hollacombe Devon 16 F11
Holland Fen Lincs 86 H11
Holland Lees Lancs 88 G9
Holland-on-Sea Essex 53 L8
Hollandstoun Ork 169 g1
Hollee D & G 110 E7
Hollesley Suffk 53 Q3
Hollicombe Torbay 7 M6
Hollingbourne Kent 38 D10
Hollingbury Br & H 24 H9
Hollingdon Bucks 49 N9
Hollingrove E Susx 25 Q6
Hollingthorpe Leeds 91 K4
Hollington Derbys 71 N7
Hollington Staffs 71 K7
Hollingworth Tamesd 83 M5
Hollins Bury 89 N9
Hollins Derbys 84 D6
Hollins Staffs 70 H5
Hollinsclough Staffs 83 N11
Hollins End Sheff 84 E4
Hollins Green Warrtn 82 E6
Hollins Lane Lancs 95 K10
Hollinswood Wrekin 57 N3
Hollinwood Shrops 69 P7
Hollocombe Devon 17 L9
Holloway Derbys 84 D9
Holloway Gt Lon 36 H3
Holloway Wilts 20 G8
Hollowell Nhants 60 E6
Hollowmoor Heath Ches W 81 P11
Hollows D & G 110 G5
Hollybush Caerph 30 G4
Hollybush E Ayrs 114 G4
Hollybush Herefs 46 E7
Holly End Norfk 75 J9
Holly Green Worcs 46 G6
Hollyhurst Ches E 69 Q6
Hollym E R Yk 93 P5
Hollywater Hants 23 M8
Hollywood Worcs 58 G9
Holmbridge Kirk 90 E9
Holmbury St Mary Surrey 24 D2
Holmbush Cnwll 3 Q3
Holmcroft Staffs 70 G10
Holme Cambs 61 Q3
Holme Cumb 95 L5
Holme Kirk 90 E9
Holme N Linc 92 F9
Holme N York 97 N4
Holme Notts 85 P9
Holme Chapel Lancs 89 P5
Holme Green N York 91 P2
Holme Hale Norfk 76 B10
Holme Lacy Herefs 45 R7
Holme Marsh Herefs 45 L4
Holme next the Sea Norfk 75 P2
Holme on the Wolds E R Yk 99 K11
Holme Pierrepont Notts 72 G3
Holmer Herefs 45 Q6
Holmer Green Bucks 35 P5
Holme St Cuthbert Cumb 109 P11
Holmes Chapel Ches E 82 G11
Holmesfield Derbys 84 D5
Holmes Hill E Susx 25 M8
Holmeswood Lancs 88 E7
Holmethorpe Surrey 36 G10
Holme upon Spalding Moor E R Yk 92 D3
Holmewood Derbys 84 F7
Holmfield Calder 90 D5
Holmfirth Kirk 90 E9
Holmgate Derbys 84 E8
Holmhead E Ayrs 115 L3
Holmpton E R Yk 93 Q6
Holmrook Cumb 100 E11
Holmshurst E Susx 25 P5
Holmside Dur 113 K11
Holmwrangle Cumb 111 K11
Holne Devon 7 J5
Holnest Dorset 11 P3
Holnicote Somset 18 B5
Holsworthy Devon 16 E11
Holsworthy Beacon Devon 16 F10
Holt Dorset 12 H4
Holt Norfk 76 F4
Holt Wilts 20 G2
Holt Worcs 46 F2
Holt Wrexhm 69 M4
Holtby C York 98 D10
Holt End Worcs 58 G11
Holt Fleet Worcs 46 F2
Holt Green Lancs 88 D9
Holt Heath Dorset 13 J4
Holt Heath Worcs 46 F2
Holton Oxon 34 H3
Holton Somset 20 C9
Holton Suffk 65 N6
Holton cum Beckering Lincs 86 F4
Holton Heath Dorset 12 F6
Holton Hill E Susx 25 Q5
Holton le Clay Lincs 93 N10
Holton le Moor Lincs 93 J11
Holton St Mary Suffk 53 J4
Holt Street Kent 39 N11
Holtye E Susx 25 L3
Holway Flints 80 H9
Holwell Dorset 11 P2
Holwell Herts 50 E4
Holwell Leics 73 J6
Holwell Oxon 33 P3
Holwick Dur 102 H5
Holworth Dorset 12 C8
Holybourne Hants 23 K6
Holy Cross Worcs 58 D9
Holyfield Essex 51 J10
Holyhead IoA 78 C8
Holy Island IoA 78 D8
Holy Island Nthumb 119 M2
Holy Island Nthumb 119 M2
Holymoorside Derbys 84 D7
Holyport W & M 35 N9
Holystone Nthumb 119 J10
Holytown N Lans 126 D5
Holywell C Beds 50 B7
Holywell Cambs 62 D6
Holywell Cnwll 4 B10
Holywell Dorset 11 M4
Holywell Flints 80 H9
Holywell Nthumb 113 M6
Holywell Warwks 59 K11
Holywell Green Calder 90 D7
Holywell Lake Somset 18 F10
Holywell Row Suffk 63 M5
Holywood D & G 109 K4
Holywood Village D & G 109 L5
Homer Shrops 57 L4
Homer Green Sefton 81 L4
Homersfield Suffk 65 K4
Homescales Cumb 95 M3
Hom Green Herefs 46 A10
Homington Wilts 21 M9
Honeyborough Pembks 40 H9
Honeybourne Worcs 47 M6
Honeychurch Devon 8 F4
Honey Hill Kent 39 K9
Honeystreet Wilts 21 M2
Honey Tye Suffk 52 G4
Honiley Warwks 59 K10
Honing Norfk 77 L6
Honingham Norfk 76 G9
Honington Lincs 73 N2
Honington Suffk 64 C7

276 Honington – Inverey

Honington Warwks 47 Q6
Honiton Devon 10 D4
Honley Kirk 90 E8
Honnington Wrekin 70 C11
Hoo Kent 39 N9
Hoobrook Worcs 58 B10
Hood Green Barns 91 J10
Hood Hill Rothm 91 K11
Hooe C Plym 6 E8
Hooe E Susx 25 Q8
Hoo End Herts 50 E6
Hoo Green Ches E 82 F8
Hoohill Bpool 88 C3
Hook Cambs 62 F2
Hook Devon 10 G3
Hook E R Yk 92 C5
Hook Gt Lon 36 E8
Hook Hants 14 F5
Hook Hants 23 K4
Hook Pembks 41 J8
Hook Wilts 33 L8
Hook-a-Gate Shrops 56 H3
Hook Bank Worcs 46 F6
Hooke Dorset 11 L4
Hook End Essex 51 N10
Hookgate Staffs 70 C7
Hook Green Kent 25 Q3
Hook Green Kent 37 P6
Hook Norton Oxon 48 C8
Hook Street Gloucs 32 C5
Hook Street Wilts 33 L8
Hookway Devon 9 L5
Hookwood Surrey 24 G2
Hooley Surrey 36 G9
Hooley Bridge Rochdl 89 P8
Hoo Meavy Devon 6 E5
Hoo St Werburgh Medway 38 C7
Hooton Ches W 81 M9
Hooton Levitt Rothm 84 H2
Hooton Pagnell Donc 91 M9
Hooton Roberts Rothm 91 M11
Hopcrofts Holt Oxon 48 E9
Hope Derbys 83 Q8
Hope Devon 6 H10
Hope Flints 69 K3
Hope Powys 56 D3
Hope Shrops 56 E4
Hope Staffs 71 L4
Hope Bagot Shrops 57 K10
Hope Bowdler Shrops 56 H6
Hope End Green Essex 51 N6
Hopehouse Border 117 K7
Hopeman Moray 157 L4
Hope Mansell Herefs 46 B11
Hopesay Shrops 56 F8
Hopetown Wakefd 91 K6
Hope under Dinmore Herefs 45 Q4
Hopgrove C York 98 C10
Hopperton N York 97 P9
Hop Pole Lincs 74 C8
Hopsford Warwks 59 P8
Hopstone Shrops 57 P6
Hopton Derbys 71 P4
Hopton Shrops 69 L10
Hopton Staffs 70 G9
Hopton Suffk 64 D6
Hopton Cangeford Shrops 57 J8
Hopton Castle Shrops 56 F9
Hoptonheath Shrops 56 F9
Hopton on Sea Norfk 65 Q2
Hopton Wafers Shrops 57 L9
Hopwas Staffs 59 J4
Hopwood Rochdl 89 P9
Hopwood Worcs 58 F9
Hopwood Park Services Worcs 58 F10
Horam E Susx 25 N7
Horbling Lincs 74 B3
Horbury Wakefd 90 H7
Horcott Gloucs 33 N4
Horden Dur 104 D2
Horderley Shrops 56 G7
Hordle Hants 13 N5
Hordley Shrops 69 L8
Horeb Carmth 28 E3
Horeb Cerdgn 42 G6
Horfield Bristl 31 Q9
Horham Suffk 65 J7
Horkesley Heath Essex 52 G6
Horkstow N Linc 92 G7
Horley Oxon 48 D6
Horley Surrey 24 G2
Hornblotton Green Somset 19 Q8
Hornby Lancs 95 M7
Hornby N York 97 K2
Hornby N York 104 C9
Horncastle Lincs 87 J7
Hornchurch Gt Lon 37 M3
Horncliffe Nthumb 129 N10
Horndean Border 129 N10
Horndean Hants 15 K4
Horndon Devon 8 D8
Horndon on the Hill Thurr 37 Q4
Horne Surrey 24 H2
Horner Somset 18 B5
Horne Row Essex 52 C11
Horners Green Suffk 52 G3
Horney Common E Susx 25 L5
Horn Hill Bucks 36 B2
Horning Norfk 77 L8
Horninghold Leics 73 L11
Horninglow Staffs 71 N9
Horningsea Cambs 62 G8
Horningsham Wilts 20 F6
Horningtoft Norfk 76 C7
Horningtops Cnwll 5 M9
Hornsbury Somset 10 G2
Hornsby Cumb 111 K10
Hornsbygate Cumb 111 K10
Horns Cross Devon 16 F7
Horns Cross E Susx 26 D7
Hornsea E R Yk 99 P11
Hornsey Gt Lon 36 H3
Horn's Green Gt Lon 37 L9
Horn Street Kent 27 L4
Hornton Oxon 48 C5
Horpit Swindn 33 P8
Horrabridge Devon 6 E5
Horringer Suffk 64 A9
Horringford IoW 14 F9
Horrocks Fold Bolton 89 L8
Horrocksford Lancs 89 M2
Horsacott Devon 17 J5
Horsebridge Devon 5 Q6
Horsebridge E Susx 25 N8
Horsebridge Hants 22 B8
Horsebridge Shrops 56 F3
Horsebridge Staffs 70 H4
Horsebrook Staffs 58 C2
Horsecastle N Som 31 M11
Horsedown Cnwll 2 G7
Horsehay Wrekin 57 M3
Horseheath Cambs 63 K11
Horsehouse N York 96 F4
Horsell Surrey 23 Q3
Horseman's Green Wrexhm 69 M6
Horsenden Bucks 35 L4
Horsey Norfk 77 P7
Horsey Somset 19 K7
Horsey Corner Norfk 77 P7
Horsford Norfk 76 H8
Horsforth Leeds 90 G3
Horsham W Susx 24 E4
Horsham Worcs 46 D3
Horsham St Faith Norfk 77 J8
Horsington Lincs 86 G7
Horsington Somset 20 D10
Horsley Derbys 72 B2
Horsley Gloucs 32 F5
Horsley Nthumb 112 G7
Horsley Nthumb 118 F11
Horsley Cross Essex 53 K6
Horsleycross Street Essex 53 K6
Horsley-Gate Derbys 84 D5
Horsleyhill Border 117 Q7
Horsley's Green Bucks 35 L6
Horsley Woodhouse Derbys 72 B2
Horsmonden Kent 26 B3
Horspath Oxon 34 G3
Horstead Norfk 77 K8
Horsted Keynes W Susx 25 J5
Horton Bucks 49 P11
Horton Dorset 12 H3
Horton Lancs 96 C10
Horton Nhants 49 M4
Horton S Glos 32 E8
Horton Shrops 69 N9
Horton Somset 10 G2
Horton Staffs 70 G3
Horton Surrey 36 E8
Horton Swans 28 E7
Horton W & M 36 B5
Horton Wilts 21 K2
Horton Wrekin 57 M2
Horton Cross Somset 19 K11
Horton-cum-Studley Oxon 34 G2
Horton Green Ches W 69 N5
Horton Heath Hants 22 E11
Horton-in-Ribblesdale N York 96 B6
Horton Kirby Kent 37 N7
Horwich Bolton 89 J8
Horwich End Derbys 83 M8
Horwood Devon 17 J6
Hoscar Lancs 88 F8
Hoscote Border 117 M8
Hose Leics 73 J5
Hosey Hill Kent 37 L10
Hosh P & K 133 P3
Hoswick Shet 169 r11
Hotham E R Yk 92 E4
Hothfield Kent 26 G3
Hoton Leics 72 F6
Hott Nthumb 111 Q3
Hough Ches E 70 C4
Hough Ches E 83 J9
Hougham Lincs 73 M2
Hough End Leeds 90 G4
Hough Green Halton 81 P7
Hough-on-the-Hill Lincs 86 B11
Houghton Cambs 62 C6
Houghton Cumb 110 H9
Houghton Hants 22 B8
Houghton Nthumb 112 H7
Houghton Pembks 41 J9
Houghton W Susx 24 B8
Houghton Conquest C Beds 50 B2
Houghton Gate Dur 113 M10
Houghton Green E Susx 26 F7
Houghton Green Warrtn 82 D6
Houghton le Side Darltn 103 P6
Houghton-le-Spring Sundld 113 M11
Houghton on the Hill Leics 72 H10
Houghton Regis C Beds 50 B6
Houghton St Giles Norfk 76 C4
Houlton Warwks 60 C6
Hound Green Hants 23 K3
Houndslow Border 128 G10
Houndsmoor Somset 18 F9
Houndwood Border 129 L7
Hounslow Gt Lon 36 D5
Househill Highld 156 F6
Houses Hill Kirk 90 F7
Housieside Abers 151 M2
Houston Rens 125 L4
Houstry Highld 167 L10
Houton Ork 169 c6
Hove Br & H 24 G10
Hove Edge Calder 90 E6
Hoveringham Notts 85 L11
Hoveton Norfk 77 L8
Hovingham N York 98 D5
How Cumb 111 K9
Howbrook Barns 91 J11
How Caple Herefs 46 B8
Howden E R Yk 92 B5
Howden-le-Wear Dur 103 N4
Howe Highld 167 P4
Howe IoM 80 a8
Howe N York 97 N4
Howe Norfk 65 K2
Howe Bridge Wigan 82 E4
Howe Green Essex 52 B11
Howegreen Essex 52 D11
Howell Lincs 86 F11
How End C Beds 50 B2
Howe of Teuchar Abers 159 J8
Howes D & G 110 C7
Howe Street Essex 51 Q4
Howe Street Essex 51 Q8
Howey Powys 44 F3
Howgate Cumb 100 C6
Howgate Mdloth 127 N6
Howgill Lancs 96 B11
Howick Nthumb 119 Q7
Howle Wrekin 70 B10
Howle Hill Herefs 46 B10
Howlett End Essex 51 N4
Howley Somset 10 F3
How Mill Cumb 111 K9
Howmore W Isls 168 c14
Hownam Border 118 E7
Howrigg Cumb 110 F11
Howsham N Linc 92 H10
Howsham N York 98 E8
Howtel Nthumb 118 G4
Howt Green Kent 38 E8
Howton Herefs 45 N9
Howtown Cumb 101 M7
How Wood Herts 50 D10
Howwood Rens 125 K5
Hoxa Ork 169 d7
Hoxne Suffk 64 H6
Hoy Ork 169 b7
Hoylake Wirral 81 J7
Hoyland Barns 91 K10
Hoyland Common Barns 91 K10
Hoylandswaine Barns 90 H10
Hoyle W Susx 23 P11
Hoyle Mill Barns 91 K9
Hubberholme N York 96 D5
Hubberston Pembks 40 G9
Hubbert's Bridge Lincs 74 E2
Huby N York 97 L11
Huby N York 98 B7
Huccaby Devon 6 H4
Hucclecote Gloucs 46 G11
Hucking Kent 38 D10
Hucknall Notts 84 H11
Huddersfield Kirk 90 E7
Huddington Worcs 46 H3
Hudnall Herts 50 B8
Hudswell N York 103 M10
Huggate E R Yk 98 H9
Hugglescote Leics 72 C8
Hughenden Valley Bucks 35 N5
Hughley Shrops 57 K5
High Town IoS 2 c2
Huish Devon 17 J9
Huish Wilts 21 M2
Huish Champflower Somset 18 E9
Huish Episcopi Somset 19 M9
Hùisinis W Isls 168 e6
Huisinish W Isls 168 e6
Hulcote C Beds 49 P7
Hulcote Nhants 49 K5
Hulcott Bucks 49 N11
Hulham Devon 9 P8
Hulland Derbys 71 N5
Hulland Ward Derbys 71 P5
Hullavington Wilts 32 G8
Hull Bridge E R Yk 93 J2
Hullbridge Essex 38 D2
Hull, Kingston upon C KuH 93 J5
Hulme Manch 82 H5
Hulme Staffs 70 G5
Hulme Warrtn 82 D6
Hulme End Staffs 71 L3
Hulme Walfield Ches E 82 H11
Hulse Heath Ches E 82 F8
Hulton Lane Ends Bolton 89 K9
Hulverstone IoW 14 C10
Hulver Street Norfk 76 C9
Hulver Street Suffk 65 P4
Humber Devon 9 L9
Humber Herefs 45 Q3
Humber Bridge N Linc 92 H6
Humberside Airport N Linc 93 J8
Humberston NE Lin 93 P9
Humberstone C Leic 72 G9
Humberton N York 97 P7
Humbie E Loth 128 D7
Humbleton E R Yk 93 M4
Humbleton Nthumb 119 J5
Humby Lincs 73 Q4
Hume Border 118 D2
Humshaugh Nthumb 112 D6
Huna Highld 167 Q2
Huncoat Lancs 89 M4
Huncote Leics 72 E11
Hundalee Border 118 B7
Hundall Derbys 84 E5
Hunderthwaite Dur 103 J6
Hundleby Lincs 87 L7
Hundle Houses Lincs 86 H10
Hundleton Pembks 41 J10
Hundon Suffk 63 M11
Hundred End Lancs 88 E6
Hundred House Powys 44 G4
Hungarton Leics 72 H9
Hungerford Hants 13 L2
Hungerford Somset 18 D6
Hungerford W Berk 34 B11
Hungerford Newtown W Berk 34 C10
Hunger Hill Bolton 89 K9
Hunger Hill Lancs 88 G8
Hungerstone Herefs 45 N7
Hungerton Lincs 73 M5
Hungryhatton Shrops 70 B9
Hunmanby N York 99 M5
Hunningham Warwks 59 N11
Hunnington Worcs 58 E8
Hunsbury Hill Nhants 60 F9
Hunsdon Herts 51 K8
Hunsdonbury Herts 51 K8
Hunsingore N York 97 P10
Hunslet Leeds 91 J4
Hunsonby Cumb 101 Q3
Hunstanton Norfk 75 N2
Hunstanworth Dur 112 D11
Hunsterson Ches E 70 B5
Hunston Suffk 64 D8
Hunston W Susx 15 N6
Hunston Green Suffk 64 D8
Hunstrete BaNES 20 B2
Hunsworth Kirk 90 F5
Hunt End Worcs 47 K2
Hunter's Inn Devon 17 M2
Hunter's Quay Ag & B 124 F2
Huntham Somset 19 K9
Hunthill Lodge Angus 142 H3
Huntingdon Cambs 62 B6
Huntingfield Suffk 65 L7
Huntingford Dorset 20 F9
Huntington C York 98 C9
Huntington Ches W 69 M2
Huntington E Loth 128 D5
Huntington Herefs 45 K4
Huntington Herefs 45 P6
Huntington Staffs 58 E2
Huntingtowerfield P & K 134 D2
Huntley Gloucs 46 D11
Huntly Abers 158 D10
Hunton Hants 22 E6
Hunton Kent 26 B2
Hunton N York 97 J2
Hunton Bridge Herts 50 C10
Hunt's Corner Norfk 64 F4
Huntscott Somset 18 B6
Hunt's Cross Lpool 81 N7
Hunts Green Bucks 35 N4
Hunts Green Warwks 59 J5
Huntsham Devon 18 D10
Huntshaw Devon 17 J7
Huntshaw Cross Devon 17 J7
Huntspill Somset 19 K5
Huntstile Somset 19 J8
Huntworth Somset 19 K8
Hunwick Dur 103 N4
Hunworth Norfk 76 F4
Hurcott Somset 19 L11
Hurdcott Wilts 21 N8
Hurdsfield Ches E 83 K10
Hurley W & M 35 M8
Hurley Warwks 59 K5
Hurley Bottom W & M 35 M8
Hurley Common Warwks 59 K5
Hurlford E Ayrs 125 M10
Hurlston Green Lancs 88 D8
Hurn BCP 13 K5
Hurn's End Lincs 87 M11
Hursley Hants 22 D9
Hurst Dorset 12 C6
Hurst N York 103 K10
Hurst Somset 19 N11
Hurst Wokham 35 L10
Hurstbourne Priors Hants 22 D5
Hurstbourne Tarrant Hants 22 C4
Hurst Green E Susx 26 B6
Hurst Green Essex 53 J8
Hurst Green Lancs 89 K3
Hurst Green Surrey 37 K10
Hurst Hill Dudley 58 D6
Hurstley Herefs 45 M5
Hurstpierpoint W Susx 24 G7
Hurst Wickham W Susx 24 G7
Hurstwood Lancs 89 P4
Hurtiso Ork 169 e6
Hurtmore Surrey 23 P5
Hurworth Burn Dur 104 D4
Hurworth-on-Tees Darltn 104 B9
Hurworth Place Darltn 103 Q9
Hury Dur 103 J7
Husbands Bosworth Leics 60 D4
Husborne Crawley C Beds 49 Q7
Husthwaite N York 97 R6
Hutcherleigh Devon 7 K8
Hut Green N York 91 P6
Huthwaite Notts 84 G9
Huttoft Lincs 87 P5
Hutton Border 129 N9
Hutton Cumb 101 M5
Hutton E R Yk 99 L10
Hutton Essex 37 P2
Hutton Lancs 88 F5
Hutton N Som 19 L3
Hutton Bonville N York 104 B10
Hutton Buscel N York 99 K4
Hutton Conyers N York 97 M6
Hutton Cranswick E R Yk 99 L10
Hutton End Cumb 101 N3
Hutton Hang N York 97 J3
Hutton Henry Dur 104 D3
Hutton-le-Hole N York 98 E2
Hutton Lowcross R & Cl 104 G8
Hutton Magna Dur 103 M8
Hutton Mulgrave N York 105 M9
Hutton Roof Cumb 95 M5
Hutton Roof Cumb 101 L4
Hutton Rudby N York 104 E9
Hutton Sessay N York 97 Q5
Hutton Wandesley N York 97 R10
Huxham Devon 9 M5
Huxham Green Somset 19 Q7
Huxley Ches W 69 P2
Huyton Knows 81 N6
Hycemoor Cumb 94 B3
Hyde Gloucs 32 G4
Hyde Hants 13 L2
Hyde Tamesd 83 K6
Hyde Heath Bucks 35 P4
Hyde Lea Staffs 70 G11
Hydestile Surrey 23 Q6
Hykeham Moor Lincs 86 B7
Hylands House & Park Essex 51 Q10
Hyndford Bridge S Lans 116 C2
Hynish Ag & B 136 B8
Hyssington Powys 56 E6
Hystfield Gloucs 32 C5
Hythe Essex 52 H6
Hythe Hants 14 D5
Hythe Kent 27 L5
Hythe Somset 19 M4
Hythe End W & M 36 B6
Hyton Cumb 94 B3

I

Ibberton Dorset 12 C3
Ible Derbys 84 B9
Ibsley Hants 13 L3
Ibstock Leics 72 C9
Ibstone Bucks 35 L6
Ibthorpe Hants 22 C4
Iburndale N York 105 N9
Ibworth Hants 22 G4
Icelton N Som 31 L11
Ichrachan Ag & B 139 J11
Ickburgh Norfk 75 R11
Ickenham Gt Lon 36 C3
Ickford Bucks 34 H3
Ickham Kent 39 M10
Ickleford Herts 50 E4
Icklesham E Susx 26 E8
Ickleton Cambs 51 L2
Icklingham Suffk 63 N6
Ickornshaw N York 90 B2
Ickwell Green C Beds 61 Q11
Icomb Gloucs 47 P10
Idbury Oxon 47 P11
Iddesleigh Devon 17 K10
Ide Devon 9 L6
Ideford Devon 9 L9
Ide Hill Kent 37 L10
Iden E Susx 26 F7
Iden Green Kent 26 B4
Iden Green Kent 26 D5
Idle C Brad 90 F3
Idless Cnwll 3 L4
Idlicote Warwks 47 Q6
Idmiston Wilts 21 N7
Idole Carmth 42 H11
Idridgehay Derbys 71 P5
Idrigill Highld 152 F5
Idstone Oxon 33 Q8
Iffley Oxon 34 F4
Ifield W Susx 24 G3
Ifold W Susx 24 B4
Iford BCP 13 K6
Iford E Susx 25 K9
Ifton Mons 31 N7
Ifton Heath Shrops 69 K7
Ightfield Shrops 69 Q7
Ightham Kent 37 N9
Iken Suffk 65 N10
Ilam Staffs 71 L4
Ilchester Somset 19 P10
Ilderton Nthumb 119 K6
Ilford Gt Lon 37 K3
Ilford Somset 19 L11
Ilfracombe Devon 17 J2
Ilkeston Derbys 72 D2
Ilketshall St Andrew Suffk 65 M4
Ilketshall St John Suffk 65 M4
Ilketshall St Lawrence Suffk 65 M5
Ilketshall St Margaret Suffk 65 L4
Ilkley C Brad 96 H11
Illand Cnwll 5 M6
Illey Dudley 58 E8
Illidge Green Ches E 70 D2
Illingworth Calder 90 D5
Illogan Cnwll 2 H5
Illston on the Hill Leics 73 J11
Ilmer Bucks 35 L3
Ilmington Warwks 47 P6
Ilminster Somset 10 H2
Ilsington Devon 9 J9
Ilsington Dorset 12 C6
Ilston Swans 28 G6
Ilton N York 97 J5
Ilton Somset 19 L11
Imachar N Ayrs 120 G3
Immingham NE Lin 93 L8
Immingham Dock NE Lin 93 L7
Impington Cambs 62 F8
Ince Ches W 81 P9
Ince Blundell Sefton 81 L4
Ince-in-Makerfield Wigan 82 C4
Inchbae Lodge Hotel Highld 155 M4
Inchbare Angus 143 L4
Inchberry Moray 157 Q6
Incheril Highld 154 D5
Inchinnan Rens 125 M4
Inchlaggan Highld 146 F7
Inchmichael P & K 134 G2
Inchmore Highld 155 Q8
Inchnadamph Highld 161 M2
Inchture P & K 134 H2
Inchyra P & K 134 F3
Indian Queens Cnwll 4 E10
Ingatestone Essex 51 P11
Ingbirchworth Barns 90 G9
Ingerthorpe N York 97 L7
Ingestre Staffs 70 H10
Ingham Lincs 86 B4
Ingham Norfk 77 M6
Ingham Suffk 64 B7
Ingham Corner Norfk 77 M6
Ingleborough Norfk 75 J7
Ingleby Derbys 72 A5
Ingleby Arncliffe N York 104 D10
Ingleby Barwick S on T 104 D8
Ingleby Cross N York 104 E10
Ingleby Greenhow N York 104 G9
Ingleigh Green Devon 8 F3
Inglesbatch BaNES 20 D2
Inglesham Swindn 33 P5
Ingleston D & G 109 L7
Ingleton Dur 103 N6
Ingleton N York 95 P6
Inglewhite Lancs 88 G3
Ingmanthorpe N York 97 P10
Ingoe Nthumb 112 F6
Ingol Lancs 88 G4
Ingoldisthorpe Norfk 75 N4
Ingoldmells Lincs 87 Q7
Ingoldsby Lincs 73 Q5
Ingram Nthumb 119 K7
Ingrave Essex 37 P2
Ingrow C Brad 90 D3
Ings Cumb 101 M11
Ingst S Glos 31 Q7
Ingthorpe Rutlnd 73 P9
Ingworth Norfk 76 H6
Inkberrow Worcs 47 K3
Inkerman Dur 103 M3
Inkersall Green Derbys 84 F6
Inkhorn Abers 159 M10
Inkpen W Berk 22 C2
Inkstack Highld 167 N2
Inmarsh Wilts 20 H2
Innellan Ag & B 124 F3
Innerleithen Border 117 L3
Innerleven Fife 135 K7
Innermessan D & G 106 E5
Innerwick E Loth 129 J5
Innesmill Moray 157 P5
Innsworth Gloucs 46 G10
Insch Abers 150 G2
Insh Highld 148 E7
Inshes Highld 156 B9
Inskip Lancs 88 F3
Inskip Moss Side Lancs 88 F3
Instow Devon 16 H5
Insworke Cnwll 6 C8
Intake Sheff 84 E4
Inver Abers 149 N9
Inver Highld 163 K10
Inver P & K 141 P9
Inverailort Highld 145 N11
Inverallign Highld 153 Q6
Inverallochy Abers 159 P4
Inveran Highld 162 D7
Inveraray Ag & B 131 M6
Inverarish Highld 153 K10
Inverarity Angus 142 H9
Inverarnan Stirlg 132 C4
Inverarnie Highld 156 B11
Inverasdale Highld 160 C10
Inverbeg Ag & B 132 C8
Inverbervie Abers 143 Q3
Inverboyndie Abers 158 G5
Invercreran Lodge Ag & B 139 J8
Inverdruie Highld 148 F5
Inveresk E Loth 127 Q3
Inveresragan Ag & B 138 H10
Inverey Abers 149 K10

Inverfarigaig – Kingsfold 277

Inverfarigaig Highld 147 N3
Inverfolla Ag & B 138 H9
Invergarry Highld 147 J7
Invergeldie P & K 133 L2
Invergloy Highld 146 G10
Invergordon Highld 156 C4
Invergowrie P & K 142 E11
Inverguseran Highld 145 M6
Inverhadden P & K 140 G6
Inverie Highld 145 N7
Inverinan Ag & B 131 K4
Inverinate Highld 145 R3
Inverkeilor Angus 143 M8
Inverkeithing Fife 134 E11
Inverkeithny Abers 158 F8
Inverkip Inver 124 G3
Inverkirkaig Highld 160 H3
Inverlael Highld 161 K9
Inverlair Highld 139 Q2
Inverliever Lodge Ag & B 130 H6
Inverlochy Ag & B 131 P2
Invermark Angus 150 C11
Invermoriston Highld 147 L4
Invernaver Highld 166 B4
Inverneill Ag & B 123 P3
Inverness Highld 156 B8
Inverness Airport Highld 156 D7
Invernettie Abers 159 R9
Invernoaden Ag & B 131 N8
Inveroran Hotel Ag & B 139 P9
Inverquharity Angus 142 G6
Inverquhomery Abers 159 P8
Inverroy Highld 146 H11
Inversanda Highld 138 G6
Invershiel Highld 146 A4
Invershin Highld 162 D7
Invershore Highld 167 M9
Inversnaid Hotel Stirlg 132 C6
Inverugie Abers 159 Q8
Inveruglas Ag & B 132 C6
Inveruglass Highld 148 E7
Inverurie Abers 151 K3
Inwardleigh Devon 8 E5
Inworth Essex 52 E8
Iochdar W Isls 168 c13
Iona Ag & B 136 H10
Iping W Susx 23 N10
iPort Logistics Park Donc 91 Q11
Ipplepen Devon 7 L5
Ipsden Oxon 34 H7
Ipstones Staffs 71 J5
Ipswich Suffk 53 L3
Irby Wirral 81 K8
Irby in the Marsh Lincs 87 N8
Irby upon Humber NE Lin 93 L10
Irchester Nhants 61 K7
Ireby Cumb 100 H3
Ireby Lancs 95 P5
Ireland C Beds 50 D2
Ireleth Cumb 94 E5
Ireshopeburn Dur 102 G3
Ireton Wood Derbys 71 P5
Irlam Salfd 82 F6
Irnham Lincs 73 Q5
Iron Acton S Glos 32 C8
Iron Bridge Cambs 75 J11
Ironbridge Wrekin 57 M4
Ironbridge Gorge Wrekin 57 M4
Iron Cross Warwks 47 L4
Ironmacannie D & G 108 E5
Irons Bottom Surrey 36 F11
Ironville Derbys 84 F10
Irstead Norfk 77 M7
Irthington Cumb 111 J8
Irthlingborough Nhants 61 K6
Irton N York 99 L4
Irvine N Ayrs 125 J10
Isauld Highld 166 G3
Isbister Shet 169 q4
Isbister Shet 169 s7
Isfield E Susx 25 K7
Isham Nhants 61 J6
Isington Hants 23 L6
Islandpool Worcs 58 C8
Islay Ag & B 122 E8
Islay Airport Ag & B 122 D9
Isle Abbotts Somset 19 L10
Isle Brewers Somset 19 L10
Isleham Cambs 63 K6
Isle of Dogs Gt Lon 37 J5
Isle of Grain Medway 38 E6
Isle of Lewis W Isls 168 i4
Isle of Man IoM 80 e4
Isle of Man Ronaldsway Airport IoM 80 c8
Isle of Mull Ag & B 137 Q8
Isle of Purbeck Dorset 12 H8
Isle of Sheppey Kent 38 G8
Isle of Skye Highld 152 G10
Isle of Thanet Kent 39 P8
Isle of Walney Cumb 94 D7
Isle of Whithorn D & G 107 N10
Isle of Wight IoW 14 F9
Isleornsay Highld 145 M5
Isles of Scilly IoS 2 c2
Isles of Scilly St Mary's Airport IoS 2 c2
Islesteps D & G 109 L6
Islet Village Guern 10 c1
Isleworth Gt Lon 36 E5
Isley Walton Leics 72 C6
Islibhig W Isls 168 f5
Islington Gt Lon 36 H4
Islip Nhants 61 L5
Islip Oxon 34 F2
Islivig W Isls 168 f5
Isombridge Wrekin 57 L2
Istead Rise Kent 37 P6
Itchen Abbas Hants 22 F8
Itchen Stoke Hants 22 G8
Itchingfield W Susx 24 D5
Itchington S Glos 32 C7
Itteringham Norfk 76 G5
Itton Devon 8 G5
Itton Mons 31 N5
Itton Common Mons 31 N5
Ivegill Cumb 101 M2
Ivelet N York 102 H11
Iver Bucks 36 B4
Iver Heath Bucks 36 B4
Iveston Dur 112 H10
Ivinghoe Bucks 49 P11
Ivinghoe Aston Bucks 49 Q11
Ivington Herefs 45 P3
Ivington Green Herefs 45 P3
Ivybridge Devon 6 G7
Ivychurch Kent 26 H6
Ivy Cross Dorset 20 G10
Ivy Hatch Kent 37 N10
Ivy Todd Norfk 76 B10
Iwade Kent 38 F8
Iwerne Courtney Dorset 12 E2
Iwerne Minster Dorset 12 E2
Ixworth Suffk 64 C7
Ixworth Thorpe Suffk 64 C7

J

Jack Green Lancs 88 H5
Jack Hill N York 97 J10
Jack-in-the-Green Devon 9 P5
Jack's Bush Hants 21 Q7
Jacksdale Notts 84 F10
Jackson Bridge Kirk 90 F9
Jackton S Lans 125 P7
Jacobstow Cnwll 5 K2
Jacobstowe Devon 8 E4
Jacobs Well Surrey 23 Q4
Jameston Pembks 41 L11
Jamestown Highld 155 N6
Jamestown W Duns 132 D11
Janetstown Highld 167 L10
Janetstown Highld 167 Q6
Jardine Hall D & G 109 P3
Jarrow S Tyne 113 M8
Jarvis Brook E Susx 25 M5
Jasper's Green Essex 52 B6
Jawcraig Falk 126 E2
Jaywick Essex 53 L9
Jealott's Hill Br For 35 N10
Jeater Houses N York 97 P2
Jedburgh Border 118 B6
Jeffreyston Pembks 41 L9
Jemimaville Highld 156 C4
Jerbourg Guern 10 c2
Jersey Jersey 11 b1
Jersey Airport Jersey 11 a2
Jersey Marine Neath 29 K6
Jerusalem Lincs 86 B6
Jesmond N u Ty 113 L7
Jevington E Susx 25 N10
Jingle Street Mons 31 N2
Jockey End Herts 50 B8
Jodrell Bank Ches E 82 G10
Jodrell Bank Ches E 82 G10
Johnby Cumb 101 M4
John Lennon Airport Lpool 81 N8
John o' Groats Highld 167 Q2
Johns Cross E Susx 26 B7
Johnshaven Abers 143 P4
Johnson Street Norfk 77 M8
Johnston Pembks 40 H8
Johnstone D & G 117 J10
Johnstone Rens 125 L5
Johnstonebridge D & G 109 P2
Johnstown Carmth 42 G11
Johnstown Wrexhm 69 K5
Joppa C Edin 127 Q3
Joppa Cerdgn 54 D11
Joppa S Ayrs 114 H4
Jordans Bucks 35 Q6
Jordanston Pembks 40 H4
Jordanthorpe Sheff 84 E4
Joyden's Wood Kent 37 M6
Jubilee Corner Kent 26 D2
Jump Barns 91 K10
Jumper's Town E Susx 25 L4
Juniper Nthumb 112 D9
Juniper Green C Edin 127 M4
Jura Ag & B 122 H3
Jurassic Coast Devon 10 G7
Jurby IoM 80 e2
Jurston Devon 8 G8

K

Kaber Cumb 102 E8
Kaimend S Lans 126 H8
Kames Ag & B 124 B3
Kames E Ayrs 115 N2
Kea Cnwll 3 L5
Keadby N Linc 92 D8
Keal Cotes Lincs 87 L8
Kearby Town End N York 97 M11
Kearsley Bolton 82 G4
Kearsley Nthumb 112 F5
Kearsney Kent 27 N3
Kearstwick Cumb 95 N5
Kearton N York 103 J11
Keasden N York 95 Q7
Keaton Devon 6 G8
Keckwick Halton 82 C8
Keddington Lincs 87 K3
Keddington Corner Lincs 87 L3
Kedington Suffk 63 M11
Kedleston Derbys 71 Q6
Keelby Lincs 93 L8
Keele Staffs 70 E5
Keele Services Staffs 70 E6
Keele University Staffs 70 E5
Keeley Green Bed 61 M11
Keelham C Brad 90 D4
Keeres Green Essex 51 N8
Keeston Pembks 40 H7
Keevil Wilts 20 H3
Kegworth Leics 72 D5
Kehelland Cnwll 2 G5
Keig Abers 150 G4
Keighley C Brad 90 D2
Keilarsbrae Clacks 133 P9
Keillour P & K 134 B2
Keiloch Abers 149 M9
Keils Ag & B 122 H6
Keinton Mandeville Somset 19 P8
Keir Mill D & G 109 J2
Keirsleywell Row Nthumb 111 Q10
Keisby Lincs 73 Q5
Keisley Cumb 102 D6
Keiss Highld 167 P4
Keith Moray 158 B7
Keithick P & K 142 C10
Keithock Angus 143 L5
Keithtown Highld 155 P6
Kelbrook Lancs 89 Q2
Kelby Lincs 73 Q2
Keld Cumb 101 Q8
Keld N York 102 G10
Keld Head N York 98 F4
Keldholme N York 98 E3
Kelfield N Linc 92 D10
Kelfield N York 91 P3
Kelham Notts 85 N9
Kelhead D & G 109 P7
Kellacott Devon 5 Q4
Kellamergh Lancs 88 E5
Kellas Angus 142 H10
Kellas Moray 157 M7
Kellaton Devon 7 L11
Kelleth Cumb 102 C9
Kelling Norfk 76 F3
Kellingley N York 91 N6
Kellington N York 91 P6
Kelloe Dur 104 B3
Kelloholm D & G 115 P5
Kells Cumb 100 C7
Kelly Devon 5 P5
Kelly Bray Cnwll 5 P7
Kelmarsh Nhants 60 F5
Kelmscott Oxon 33 P5
Kelsale Suffk 65 M8
Kelsall Ches W 81 Q11
Kelshall Herts 50 H3
Kelsick Cumb 110 C10
Kelso Border 118 D4
Kelstedge Derbys 84 D8
Kelstern Lincs 86 H3
Kelsterton Flints 81 K10
Kelston BaNES 32 D11
Keltneyburn P & K 141 J8
Kelton D & G 109 L6
Kelty Fife 134 E9
Kelvedon Essex 52 E8
Kelvedon Hatch Essex 51 N11
Kelynack Cnwll 2 B8
Kemacott Devon 17 M2
Kemback Fife 135 L5
Kemberton Shrops 57 N4
Kemble Gloucs 33 J5
Kemble Wick Gloucs 33 J5
Kemerton Worcs 47 J7
Kemeys Commander Mons 31 K4
Kemnay Abers 151 J4
Kempe's Corner Kent 26 H2
Kempley Gloucs 46 C9
Kempley Green Gloucs 46 C9
Kempsey Worcs 46 F5
Kempsford Gloucs 33 N5
Kemps Green Warwks 58 H10
Kempshott Hants 22 H4
Kempston Bed 61 M11
Kempston Hardwick Bed 50 B2
Kempton Shrops 56 F8
Kemp Town Br & H 24 H10
Kemsing Kent 37 N9
Kemsley Kent 38 F8
Kemsley Street Kent 38 D9
Kenardington Kent 26 G5
Kenchester Herefs 45 N6
Kencot Oxon 33 Q4
Kendal Cumb 95 L2
Kenderchurch Herefs 45 N9
Kendleshire S Glos 32 C9
Kenfig Brdgnd 29 M8
Kenfig Hill Brdgnd 29 M8
Kenilworth Warwks 59 L10
Kenley Gt Lon 36 H8
Kenley Shrops 57 K4
Kenmore Highld 153 P6
Kenmore P & K 141 J8
Kenn Devon 9 M7
Kenn N Som 31 M11
Kennacraig Ag & B 123 P7
Kennall Vale Cnwll 3 J6
Kennards House Cnwll 5 M5
Kenneggy Cnwll 2 F8
Kennerleigh Devon 9 K3
Kennet Clacks 133 Q9
Kennethmont Abers 150 E2
Kennett Cambs 63 L7
Kennford Devon 9 M7
Kenninghall Norfk 64 E4
Kennington Kent 26 H2
Kennington Oxon 34 F4
Kennington Lees Kent 26 H2
Kennoway Fife 135 K7
Kenny Somset 19 K11
Kenny Hill Suffk 63 L5
Kennythorpe N York 98 F7
Kenovay Ag & B 136 B6
Kensaleyre Highld 152 G7
Kensington Gt Lon 36 G5
Kensington Palace Gt Lon 36 G4
Kensworth Common C Beds 50 B7
Kentallen Highld 139 J6
Kentchurch Herefs 45 N9
Kentford Suffk 63 M7
Kent Green Ches E 70 E3
Kentisbeare Devon 9 Q3
Kentisbury Devon 17 L3
Kentisbury Ford Devon 17 L3
Kentish Town Gt Lon 36 G4
Kentmere Cumb 101 N10
Kenton Devon 9 N8
Kenton Gt Lon 36 E3
Kenton N u Ty 113 K7
Kenton Suffk 64 H8
Kenton Bankfoot N u Ty 113 K7
Kentra Highld 138 B4
Kents Bank Cumb 94 H5
Kentsboro Hants 22 B7
Kent's Green Gloucs 46 D10
Kent's Oak Hants 22 B10
Kent Street E Susx 26 C8
Kent Street Kent 37 Q10
Kenwick Shrops 69 M8
Kenwyn Cnwll 3 L4
Kenyon Warrtn 82 D5
Keoldale Highld 165 J3
Keppoch Highld 145 Q3
Kepwick N York 97 Q2
Keresley Covtry 59 M8
Kermincham Ches E 82 H11
Kernborough Devon 7 K10
Kerne Bridge Herefs 46 A11
Kerrera Ag & B 130 G2
Kerridge Ches E 83 K9
Kerridge-end Ches E 83 K9
Kerris Cnwll 2 C8
Kerry Powys 55 Q6
Kerrycroy Ag & B 124 E5
Kersall Notts 85 M8
Kersbrook Devon 9 Q8
Kerscott Devon 17 L6
Kersey Suffk 52 H3
Kersey Tye Suffk 52 G3
Kersey Upland Suffk 52 G3
Kershader W Isls 168 i6
Kershopefoot Cumb 111 J4
Kersoe Worcs 47 J6
Kerswell Devon 10 B3
Kerswell Green Worcs 46 G5
Kerthen Wood Cnwll 2 F7
Kesgrave Suffk 53 M2
Kessingland Suffk 65 Q4
Kessingland Beach Suffk 65 Q4
Kestle Cnwll 3 P4
Kestle Mill Cnwll 4 C10
Keston Gt Lon 37 K8
Keswick Cumb 101 J6
Keswick Norfk 77 J11
Ketsby Lincs 87 L5
Kettering Nhants 61 J5
Ketteringham Norfk 76 H11
Kettins P & K 142 C10
Kettlebaston Suffk 64 D11
Kettlebridge Fife 135 J6
Kettlebrook Staffs 59 K4
Kettleburgh Suffk 65 K9
Kettle Green Herts 51 K7
Kettleholm D & G 109 P5
Kettleness N York 105 M7
Kettleshulme Ches E 83 L9
Kettlesing N York 97 K9
Kettlesing Bottom N York 97 K9
Kettlestone Norfk 76 D5
Kettlethorpe Lincs 85 P5
Kettletoft Ork 169 f3
Kettlewell N York 96 E6
Ketton Rutlnd 73 P10
Kew Gt Lon 36 E5
Kew Royal Botanic Gardens Gt Lon 36 E5
Kewstoke N Som 19 K2
Kexbrough Barns 91 J9
Kexby C York 98 E10
Kexby Lincs 85 Q3
Key Green Ches E 70 F2
Key Green N York 105 M10
Keyham Leics 72 H9
Keyhaven Hants 13 P6
Keyingham E R Yk 93 M5
Keymer W Susx 24 H7
Keynsham BaNES 32 C11
Keysoe Bed 61 N8
Keysoe Row Bed 61 N8
Keyston Cambs 61 M5
Key Street Kent 38 E9
Keyworth Notts 72 G4
Kibbear Somset 18 H10
Kibblesworth Gatesd 113 K9
Kibworth Beauchamp Leics 60 E2
Kibworth Harcourt Leics 60 E2
Kidbrooke Gt Lon 37 K5
Kidburngill Cumb 100 E6
Kiddemore Green Staffs 58 C3
Kidderminster Worcs 58 B9
Kiddington Oxon 48 D10
Kidd's Moor Norfk 76 G11
Kidlington Oxon 34 E2
Kidmore End Oxon 35 J9
Kidsdale D & G 107 M10
Kidsgrove Staffs 70 E4
Kidstones N York 96 E4
Kidwelly Carmth 28 D3
Kiel Crofts Ag & B 138 G10
Kielder Nthumb 111 M2
Kielder Forest 111 M3
Kiells Ag & B 122 F6
Kilbarchan Rens 125 L5
Kilbeg Highld 145 L6
Kilberry Ag & B 123 M7
Kilbirnie N Ayrs 125 J7
Kilbride Ag & B 123 M4
Kilbride Ag & B 124 C4
Kilbuiack Moray 157 K5
Kilburn Derbys 84 E11
Kilburn Gt Lon 36 F4
Kilburn N York 97 R5
Kilby Leics 72 G11
Kilchamaig Ag & B 123 P7
Kilchattan Ag & B 124 E7
Kilchattan Ag & B 136 b2
Kilcheran Ag & B 138 E10
Kilchoan Highld 137 M3
Kilchoman Ag & B 122 B7
Kilchrenan Ag & B 131 L3
Kilconquhar Fife 135 M7
Kilcot Gloucs 46 C9
Kilcoy Highld 155 Q7
Kilcreggan Ag & B 131 Q11
Kildale N York 104 H9
Kildalloig Ag & B 120 E8
Kildary Highld 156 D3
Kildavaig Ag & B 124 B4
Kildavanan Ag & B 124 C4
Kildonan Highld 163 L2
Kildonan N Ayrs 121 K7
Kildonan Lodge Highld 163 L2
Kildonnan Highld 144 G10
Kildrochet House D & G 106 E6
Kildrummy Abers 150 D4
Kildwick N York 96 F11
Kilfinan Ag & B 124 A2
Kilfinnan Highld 146 H8
Kilford Denbgs 80 F11
Kilgetty Pembks 41 M9
Kilgrammie S Ayrs 114 E7
Kilgwrrwg Common Mons 31 N5
Kilham E R Yk 99 M8
Kilham Nthumb 118 G4
Kilkenneth Ag & B 136 A7
Kilkenzie Ag & B 120 C7
Kilkerran Ag & B 120 D8
Kilkhampton Cnwll 16 D9
Killamarsh Derbys 84 G4
Killay Swans 28 H6
Killearn Stirlg 132 G10
Killen Highld 156 B6
Killerby Darltn 103 N7
Killerton Devon 9 N4
Killichonan P & K 140 D6
Killiechonate Highld 146 G11
Killiechronan Ag & B 137 N7
Killiecrankie P & K 141 M5
Killilan Highld 154 B11
Killimster Highld 167 P5
Killin Stirlg 140 E11
Killinghall N York 97 L9
Killington Cumb 95 N3
Killington Devon 17 M2
Killington Lake Services Cumb 95 M2
Killingworth N Tyne 113 L6
Killiow Cnwll 3 L5
Killochyett Border 128 D10
Kilmacolm Inver 125 K3
Kilmahog Stirlg 133 J6
Kilmahumaig Ag & B 130 F9
Kilmaluag Highld 152 G3
Kilmany Fife 135 K3
Kilmarnock E Ayrs 125 L10
Kilmartin Ag & B 130 G8
Kilmaurs E Ayrs 125 L9
Kilmelford Ag & B 130 H5
Kilmersdon Somset 20 C4
Kilmeston Hants 22 G9
Kilmichael Ag & B 120 C7
Kilmichael Glassary Ag & B 130 H9
Kilmichael of Inverlussa Ag & B 130 F10
Kilmington Devon 10 F5
Kilmington Wilts 20 E7
Kilmington Common Wilts 20 E7
Kilmington Street Wilts 20 E7
Kilmorack Highld 155 N9
Kilmore Ag & B 130 H2
Kilmore Highld 145 L6
Kilmory Ag & B 123 M5
Kilmory Highld 137 N2
Kilmory N Ayrs 121 J7
Kilmuir Highld 152 D8
Kilmuir Highld 152 F3
Kilmuir Highld 156 B8
Kilmuir Highld 156 D3
Kilmun Ag & B 131 P11
Kilnave Ag & B 122 C5
Kilncadzow S Lans 126 F8
Kilndown Kent 26 B4
Kiln Green Wokham 35 M9
Kilnhill Cumb 100 H4
Kilnhurst Rothm 91 M11
Kilninver Ag & B 130 G3
Kiln Pit Hill Nthumb 112 F9
Kilnsea E R Yk 93 R7
Kilnsey N York 96 E7
Kilnwick E R Yk 99 K11
Kilnwick Percy E R Yk 98 G10
Kilnwood Vale W Susx 24 F4
Kiloran Ag & B 136 b2
Kilpatrick N Ayrs 120 H6
Kilpeck Herefs 45 N8
Kilpin E R Yk 92 C5
Kilpin Pike E R Yk 92 C5
Kilrenny Fife 135 P7
Kilsby Nhants 60 C6
Kilspindie P & K 134 G2
Kilstay D & G 106 F10
Kilsyth N Lans 126 C2
Kiltarlity Highld 155 P9
Kilton R & Cl 105 K7
Kilton Somset 18 G6
Kilton Thorpe R & Cl 105 J7
Kilvaxter Highld 152 F4
Kilve Somset 18 F6
Kilvington Notts 73 L2
Kilwinning N Ayrs 125 J9
Kimberley Norfk 76 F11
Kimberley Notts 72 D2
Kimberworth Rothm 84 F2
Kimblesworth Dur 113 L11
Kimble Wick Bucks 35 M3
Kimbolton Cambs 61 P7
Kimbolton Herefs 45 Q2
Kimcote Leics 60 C3
Kimmeridge Dorset 12 F9
Kimmerston Nthumb 119 J3
Kimpton Hants 21 Q5
Kimpton Herts 50 E7
Kimworthy Devon 16 E9
Kinbrace Highld 166 E10
Kinbuck Stirlg 133 M6
Kincaple Fife 135 M4
Kincardine Fife 133 Q10
Kincardine Highld 162 E9
Kincardine Bridge Fife 133 Q10
Kincardine O'Neil Abers 150 F8
Kinclaven P & K 142 B10
Kincorth C Aber 151 N7
Kincorth House Moray 157 J5
Kincraig Highld 148 E6
Kincraigie P & K 141 N8
Kindallachan P & K 141 N8
Kinerarach Ag & B 123 L9
Kineton Gloucs 47 L9
Kineton Warwks 48 B4
Kinfauns P & K 134 F3
Kingarth Ag & B 124 D6
Kingcausie Abers 151 M8
Kingcoed Mons 31 M3
Kingerby Lincs 86 E2
Kingford Devon 16 D10
Kingham Oxon 47 Q10
Kingholm Quay D & G 109 L6
Kinghorn Fife 134 H10
Kinglassie Fife 134 G8
Kingoodie P & K 135 J2
King's Acre Herefs 45 P6
Kingsand Cnwll 6 C8
Kingsash Bucks 35 N3
Kingsbarns Fife 135 P5
Kingsborough Kent 38 G7
Kingsbridge Devon 7 J10
Kingsbridge Somset 18 C7
Kingsbridge Swans 28 G5
King's Bromley Staffs 71 L11
Kingsbrook Bucks 35 M2
Kingsburgh Highld 152 F6
Kingsbury Gt Lon 36 E3
Kingsbury Warwks 59 K5
Kingsbury Episcopi Somset 19 M10
King's Caple Herefs 45 R9
Kingsclere Hants 22 F3
King's Cliffe Nhants 73 Q11
Kings Clipstone Notts 85 K8
Kingscote Gloucs 32 F5
Kingscott Devon 17 J8
King's Coughton Warwks 47 L3
Kingscross N Ayrs 121 K6
Kingsdon Somset 19 P9
Kingsdown Kent 27 Q2
Kingsdown Swindn 33 N7
Kingsdown Wilts 32 F11
Kingseat Abers 151 N4
Kingseat Fife 134 E9
Kingsey Bucks 35 K3
Kingsfold W Susx 24 E3

Port Mulgrave – Redmain 289

Port Mulgrave N York 105 L7
Portnacroish Ag & B 138 G8
Portnaguran W Isls 168 k4
Portnahaven Ag & B 122 A9
Portnalong Highld 152 E11
Portnancon Highld 165 K4
Port nan Giùran W Isls 168 k4
Port nan Long W Isls 168 d10
Port Nis W Isls 168 k1
Portobello C Edin 127 Q3
Portobello Gatesd 113 L9
Portobello Wolves 58 E5
Port of Menteith Stirlg 132 H7
Port of Ness W Isls 168 k1
Porton Wilts 21 N7
Portontown Devon 5 Q6
Portpatrick D & G 106 C7
Port Quin Cnwll 4 F5
Port Ramsay Ag & B 138 F8
Portreath Cnwll 2 H4
Portreath Harbour Cnwll 2 H4
Portree Highld 152 H9
Port Righ Ag & B 120 F4
Port St Mary IoM 80 b8
Portscatho Cnwll 3 M6
Portsea C Port 14 H6
Portskerra Highld 166 E3
Portskewett Mons 31 N7
Portslade Br & H 24 G9
Portslade-by-Sea Br & H 24 G9
Portslogan D & G 106 C6
Portsmouth C Port 14 H7
Portsmouth Calder 89 Q5
Portsmouth Arms Devon 17 L8
Portsmouth Dockyard C Port 14 H6
Port Soderick IoM 80 d7
Port Solent C Port 14 H5
Portsonachan Hotel Ag & B 131 L3
Portsoy Abers 158 E4
Port Sunlight Wirral 81 L8
Portswood C Sotn 14 D4
Port Talbot Neath 29 L7
Port Tennant Swans 29 J6
Portuairk Highld 137 L2
Portway Herefs 45 P6
Portway Herefs 45 P7
Portway Sandw 58 E7
Portway Worcs 58 G10
Port Wemyss Ag & B 122 A9
Port William D & G 107 K9
Portwrinkle Cnwll 5 P11
Portyerrock D & G 107 N10
Posbury Devon 9 K5
Posenhall Shrops 57 M4
Poslingford Suffk 63 N11
Posso Border 117 J4
Postbridge Devon 8 G9
Postcombe Oxon 35 K4
Post Green Dorset 12 G6
Postling Kent 27 K4
Postwick Norfk 77 K10
Potarch Abers 150 G8
Potsgrove C Beds 49 Q8
Potten End Herts 50 B9
Potten Street Kent 39 N8
Potter Brompton N York 99 K5
Pottergate Street Norfk 64 H3
Potterhanworth Lincs 86 E7
Potterhanworth Booths Lincs 86 E7
Potter Heigham Norfk 77 N8
Potterne Wilts 21 J3
Potterne Wick Wilts 21 J3
Potter Row Bucks 35 P4
Potters Bar Herts 50 F10
Potters Brook Lancs 95 K10
Potters Corner Kent 26 G3
Potter's Cross Staffs 58 B8
Potters Crouch Herts 50 D9
Potter's Forstal Kent 26 E2
Potters Green Covtry 59 N8
Potter's Green E Susx 25 M6
Potter's Green Herts 51 J6
Pottersheath Herts 50 F7
Potters Marston Leics 72 D11
Potter Somersal Derbys 71 L7
Potterspury Nhants 49 L6
Potter Street Essex 51 L9
Potterton Abers 151 N4
Potterton Leeds 91 L3
Potthorpe Norfk 76 C7
Pottle Street Wilts 20 F6
Potto N York 104 E10
Potton C Beds 62 B11
Pott Row Norfk 75 P6
Pott's Green Essex 52 F7
Pott Shrigley Ches E 83 K9
Poughill Cnwll 16 C10
Poughill Devon 9 L3
Poulner Hants 13 L3
Poulshot Wilts 21 J3
Poulton Gloucs 33 L4
Poulton Wirral 81 L6
Poulton-le-Fylde Lancs 88 C3
Poulton Priory Gloucs 33 L5
Pound Bank Worcs 57 N10
Poundbury Dorset 11 P6
Poundffald Swans 28 G6
Poundgate E Susx 25 L5
Pound Green E Susx 25 M6
Pound Green Suffk 63 M10
Pound Green Worcs 57 P9
Pound Hill W Susx 24 G3
Poundon Bucks 48 H9
Poundsbridge Kent 25 M2
Poundsgate Devon 7 J4
Poundstock Cnwll 5 L2
Pound Street Hants 22 E2
Pounsley E Susx 25 M6
Pouton D & G 107 N8
Pouy Street Suffk 65 M7
Povey Cross Surrey 24 G2
Powburn Nthumb 119 L7
Powderham Devon 9 N8
Powerstock Dorset 11 L5
Powfoot D & G 109 P7
Pow Green Herefs 46 D6
Powhill Cumb 110 D9
Powick Worcs 46 F4
Powmill P & K 134 C8
Poxwell Dorset 12 B8
Poyle Slough 36 B5
Poynings W Susx 24 G8
Poyntington Dorset 20 C10
Poynton Ches E 83 K8
Poynton Wrekin 69 Q11
Poynton Green Wrekin 69 Q11
Poyston Cross Pembks 41 J7
Poystreet Green Suffk 64 D10
Praa Sands Cnwll 2 F8
Pratt's Bottom Gt Lon 37 L8
Praze-an-Beeble Cnwll 2 G6
Predannack Wollas Cnwll 2 H10
Prees Shrops 69 Q8
Preesall Lancs 94 H11
Prees Green Shrops 69 Q8
Preesgweene Shrops 69 J7
Prees Heath Shrops 69 Q7
Prees Higher Heath Shrops 69 Q7
Prees Lower Heath Shrops 69 Q8
Prendwick Nthumb 119 K8
Pren-gwyn Cerdgn 42 H6
Prenteg Gwynd 67 K6
Prenton Wirral 81 L7
Prescot Knows 81 P6
Prescott Devon 10 B2
Prescott Shrops 57 M8
Prescott Shrops 69 M10
Presnerb Angus 142 B4
Pressen Nthumb 118 F3
Prestatyn Denbgs 80 F8
Prestbury Ches E 83 J9
Prestbury Gloucs 47 J10
Presteigne Powys 45 L2
Prestleigh Somset 20 B6
Prestolee Bolton 89 M9
Preston Border 129 K8
Preston Br & H 24 H9
Preston Devon 7 M4
Preston Dorset 11 Q8
Preston E R Yk 93 L4
Preston Gloucs 33 K4
Preston Herts 50 E6
Preston Kent 38 H9
Preston Kent 39 M9
Preston Lancs 88 G5
Preston Nthumb 119 N5
Preston RutInd 73 M10
Preston Shrops 57 J2
Preston Somset 18 E7
Preston Torbay 7 M6
Preston Wilts 33 K9
Preston Wilts 33 Q10
Preston Bagot Warwks 59 J11
Preston Bissett Bucks 49 J9
Preston Bowyer Somset 18 F9
Preston Brockhurst Shrops 69 P10
Preston Brook Halton 82 C8
Preston Candover Hants 22 H6
Preston Capes Nhants 48 G4
Preston Crowmarsh Oxon 34 H6
Preston Deanery Nhants 60 G9
Preston Green Warwks 59 J11
Preston Gubbals Shrops 69 N11
Preston Montford Shrops 56 G2
Preston on Stour Warwks 47 P5
Preston on Tees S on T 104 D7
Preston on the Hill Halton 82 C8
Preston on Wye Herefs 45 M6
Prestonpans E Loth 128 B5
Preston Patrick Cumb 95 L4
Preston Plucknett Somset 19 P11
Preston St Mary Suffk 64 C11
Preston Street Kent 39 N9
Preston-under-Scar N York 96 G2
Preston upon the Weald Moors Wrekin 70 B11
Preston Wynne Herefs 45 R5
Prestwich Bury 82 H4
Prestwick Nthumb 113 J6
Prestwick S Ayrs 114 G2
Prestwick Airport S Ayrs 114 G2
Prestwood Bucks 35 N4
Prestwood Staffs 58 C7
Price Town Brdgnd 29 P6
Prickwillow Cambs 63 J4
Priddy Somset 19 P4
Priestacott Devon 8 B3
Priestcliffe Derbys 83 P10
Priestcliffe Ditch Derbys 83 P10
Priest Hutton Lancs 95 L6
Priestland E Ayrs 125 P10
Priestley Green Calder 90 E5
Priest Weston Shrops 56 D5
Priestwood Green Kent 37 Q8
Primethorpe Leics 60 B2
Primrose Green Norfk 76 F8
Primrosehill Border 129 K8
Primrose Hill Cambs 62 E3
Primrose Hill Derbys 84 F9
Primrose Hill Dudley 58 D7
Primrose Hill Lancs 88 D9
Primsidemill Border 118 F5
Prince of Wales Bridge Mons 31 P7
Princes Gate Pembks 41 M8
Princes Risborough Bucks 35 M4
Princethorpe Warwks 59 P10
Princetown Devon 6 F4
Prinsted W Susx 15 L5
Prion Denbgs 68 E2
Prior Rigg Cumb 111 J7
Priors Halton Shrops 56 H9
Priors Hardwick Warwks 48 E3
Priorslee Wrekin 57 N2
Priors Marston Warwks 48 E3
Priors Norton Gloucs 46 G10
Priors Park Gloucs 46 G8
Priory Wood Herefs 45 K5
Prisk V Glam 30 D9
Priston BaNES 20 C2
Pristow Green Norfk 64 G4
Prittlewell Sthend 38 E4
Privett Hants 23 J9
Prixford Devon 17 K4
Probus Cnwll 3 M4
Prora E Loth 128 E4
Prospect Cumb 100 F2
Prospidnick Cnwll 2 G7
Protstonhill Abers 159 K5
Prudhoe Nthumb 112 G8
Prussia Cove Cnwll 2 F8
Pubil P & K 140 C9
Publow BaNES 20 B2
Puckeridge Herts 51 J6
Puckington Somset 19 L11
Pucklechurch S Glos 32 C9
Puckrup Gloucs 46 G7
Puddinglake Ches W 82 F11
Puddington Ches W 81 L10
Puddington Devon 9 K2
Puddledock Norfk 64 F3
Puddletown Dorset 12 C6
Pudleston Herefs 45 R3
Pudsey Leeds 90 G4
Pulborough W Susx 24 B7
Puleston Wrekin 70 C10
Pulford Ches W 69 L3
Pulham Dorset 11 Q3
Pulham Market Norfk 64 H4
Pulham St Mary Norfk 65 J4
Pullens Green S Glos 32 B6
Pulloxhill C Beds 50 C4
Pulverbatch Shrops 56 G4
Pumpherston W Loth 127 K4
Pumsaint Carmth 43 N6
Puncheston Pembks 41 K5
Puncknowle Dorset 11 L7
Punnett's Town E Susx 25 P6
Purbrook Hants 15 J5
Purfleet-on-Thames Thurr 37 N5
Puriton Somset 19 K6
Purleigh Essex 52 D11
Purley Gt Lon 36 H8
Purley on Thames W Berk 35 J9
Purlogue Shrops 56 D9
Purlpit Wilts 32 G11
Purls Bridge Cambs 62 G3
Purse Caundle Dorset 20 C11
Purshull Green Worcs 58 C10
Purslow Shrops 56 F8
Purston Jaglin Wakefd 91 L7
Purtington Somset 10 H3
Purton Gloucs 32 C3
Purton Gloucs 32 C4
Purton Wilts 33 L7
Purton Stoke Wilts 33 L6
Pury End Nhants 49 K5
Pusey Oxon 34 C5
Putley Herefs 46 B7
Putley Green Herefs 46 B7
Putloe Gloucs 32 E3
Putney Gt Lon 36 F6
Putsborough Devon 16 G3
Puttenham Herts 35 N2
Puttenham Surrey 23 P5
Puttock End Essex 52 D3
Putton Dorset 11 N8
Putts Corner Devon 10 C5
Puxley Nhants 49 L6
Puxton N Som 19 M2
Pwll Carmth 28 E4
Pwllcrochan Pembks 40 H10
Pwll-du Mons 30 H2
Pwll-glâs Denbgs 68 F4
Pwllgloyw Powys 44 E8
Pwllheli Gwynd 66 F7
Pwllmeyric Mons 31 P6
Pwll-trap Carmth 41 Q7
Pwll-y-glaw Neath 29 L6
Pydew Conwy 79 Q9
Pye Bridge Derbys 84 F10
Pyecombe W Susx 24 G8
Pye Corner Newpt 31 K7
Pye Green Staffs 58 E2
Pyle Brdgnd 29 M8
Pyleigh Somset 18 F8
Pylle Somset 20 B7
Pymoor Cambs 62 G3
Pymore Dorset 11 K6
Pyrford Surrey 36 B9
Pyrton Oxon 35 J5
Pytchley Nhants 61 J6
Pyworthy Devon 16 E11

Q

Quabbs Shrops 56 C8
Quadring Lincs 74 D4
Quadring Eaudike Lincs 74 D4
Quainton Bucks 49 K10
Quaker's Yard Myr Td 30 E5
Quaking Houses Dur 113 J10
Quantock Hills Somset 18 G7
Quarff Shet 169 r10
Quarley Hants 21 Q6
Quarndon Derbys 72 A2
Quarr Hill IoW 14 G8
Quarrier's Village Inver 125 K4
Quarrington Lincs 73 R2
Quarrington Hill Dur 104 B3
Quarrybank Ches W 82 C11
Quarry Bank Dudley 58 D7
Quarrywood Moray 157 M5
Quarter N Ayrs 124 F5
Quarter S Lans 126 C7
Quatford Shrops 57 N6
Quatt Shrops 57 P7
Quebec Dur 103 N2
Quedgeley Gloucs 32 F2
Queen Adelaide Cambs 63 J4
Queenborough Kent 38 F7
Queen Camel Somset 19 Q10
Queen Charlton BaNES 32 B11
Queen Dart Devon 17 Q8
Queen Elizabeth Forest Park Stirlg 132 G7
Queen Elizabeth II Bridge Thurr 37 N5
Queenhill Worcs 46 G7
Queen Oak Dorset 20 E8
Queen's Bower IoW 14 G10
Queensbury C Brad 90 E4
Queensferry Flints 81 L11
Queensferry Crossing Fife 134 E11
Queen's Head Shrops 69 K9
Queen's Hills Norfk 76 H9
Queenslie C Glas 126 B4
Queen's Park Bed 61 M11
Queen's Park Essex 51 Q11
Queen's Park Nhants 60 G8
Queen Street Kent 37 Q11
Queen Street Wilts 33 K7
Queenzieburn N Lans 126 B2
Quendon Essex 51 M4
Queniborough Leics 72 G8
Quenington Gloucs 33 M4
Quernmore Lancs 95 L9
Queslett Birm 58 G6
Quethiock Cnwll 5 N9
Quick's Green W Berk 34 G9
Quidenham Norfk 64 E4
Quidhampton Hants 22 F4
Quidhampton Wilts 21 M8
Quina Brook Shrops 69 P8
Quinbury End Nhants 48 H4
Quinton Dudley 58 E8
Quinton Nhants 49 L4
Quinton Green Nhants 49 L4
Quintrell Downs Cnwll 4 C9
Quixhall Staffs 71 L6
Quixwood Border 129 K7
Quoditch Devon 5 Q2
Quoig P & K 133 N3
Quorn Leics 72 F7
Quothquan S Lans 116 D3
Quoyburray Ork 169 e6
Quoyloo Ork 169 b4

R

Raasay Highld 153 K9
Rabbit's Cross Kent 26 C2
Rableyheath Herts 50 F7
Raby Cumb 110 C10
Raby Wirral 81 L9
Rachan Mill Border 116 G4
Rachub Gwynd 79 L11
Rackenford Devon 17 R8
Rackham W Susx 24 B8
Rackheath Norfk 77 K9
Racks D & G 109 M6
Rackwick Ork 169 b7
Radbourne Derbys 71 P7
Radcliffe Bury 89 M9
Radcliffe Nthumb 119 Q10
Radcliffe on Trent Notts 72 G3
Radclive Bucks 49 J8
Radcot Oxon 33 Q5
Raddery Highld 156 C6
Raddington Somset 18 D9
Radernie Fife 135 M6
Radford Covtry 59 M8
Radford Semele Warwks 48 B2
Radlet Somset 18 H7
Radlett Herts 50 E10
Radley Devon 17 N7
Radley Oxon 34 F5
Radley W Berk 34 C11
Radley Green Essex 51 P9
Radmore Green Ches E 69 Q3
Radnage Bucks 35 L5
Radstock BaNES 20 C4
Radstone Nhants 48 G6
Radway Warwks 48 C5
Radwell Bed 61 M9
Radwell Herts 50 F3
Radwinter Essex 51 P3
Radwinter End Essex 51 P3
Radyr Cardif 30 F8
RAF College (Cranwell) Lincs 86 D11
Rafford Moray 157 K6
RAF Museum Cosford Shrops 57 P3
RAF Museum Hendon Gt Lon 36 F2
Ragdale Leics 72 H7
Ragdon Shrops 56 H6
Raginnis Cnwll 2 D8
Raglan Mons 31 M3
Ragnall Notts 85 P6
Raigbeg Highld 148 E2
Rainbow Hill Worcs 46 G3
Rainford St Hel 81 P4
Rainford Junction St Hel 81 P4
Rainham Gt Lon 37 M4
Rainham Medway 38 D8
Rainhill St Hel 81 P6
Rainhill Stoops St Hel 81 Q6
Rainow Ches E 83 K9
Rainsough Bury 82 H4
Rainton N York 97 N5
Rainworth Notts 85 J9
Raisbeck Cumb 102 B9
Raise Cumb 111 P11
Raisthorpe N York 98 H8
Rait P & K 134 G2
Raithby Lincs 87 K4
Raithby Lincs 87 L7
Raithwaite N York 105 N8
Rake Hants 23 M9
Rakewood Rochdl 89 Q8
Ralia Highld 148 C8
Ram Carmth 43 L5
Ramasaig Highld 152 B9
Rame Cnwll 3 J7
Rame Cnwll 6 C9
Ram Hill S Glos 32 C9
Ram Lane Kent 26 G2
Rampisham Dorset 11 M4
Rampside Cumb 94 E7
Rampton Cambs 62 F7
Rampton Notts 85 P5
Ramsbottom Bury 89 M7
Ramsbury Wilts 33 Q10
Ramscraigs Highld 167 K11
Ramsdean Hants 23 K10
Ramsdell Hants 22 G3
Ramsden Oxon 48 C11
Ramsden Worcs 46 H5
Ramsden Bellhouse Essex 38 B3
Ramsden Heath Essex 38 B2
Ramsey Cambs 62 C3
Ramsey Essex 53 M5
Ramsey IoM 80 g3
Ramsey Forty Foot Cambs 62 D3
Ramsey Heights Cambs 62 B4
Ramsey Island Essex 52 F10
Ramsey Island Pembks 40 D6
Ramsey Mereside Cambs 62 C3
Ramsey St Mary's Cambs 62 C3
Ramsgate Kent 39 Q8
Ramsgill N York 96 H6
Ramshaw Dur 103 M5
Ramshaw Dur 112 E11
Ramsholt Suffk 53 P3
Ramshope Nthumb 118 D10
Ramshorn Staffs 71 K5
Ramsley Devon 8 G6
Ramsnest Common Surrey 23 P8
Ranby Lincs 86 H5
Ranby Notts 85 L4
Rand Lincs 86 F5
Randwick Gloucs 32 F3
Ranfurly Rens 125 K4
Rangemore Staffs 71 M10
Rangeworthy S Glos 32 C7
Rankinston E Ayrs 115 J5
Ranksborough RutInd 73 L8
Rank's Green Essex 52 B8
Rannoch Station P & K 140 B6
Ranscombe Somset 18 B6
Ranskill Notts 85 L3
Ranton Staffs 70 F10
Ranton Green Staffs 70 E10
Ranworth Norfk 77 M9
Raploch Stirlg 133 M9
Rapness Ork 169 e2
Rapps Somset 19 K11
Rascarrel D & G 108 G11
Rashfield Ag & B 131 N11
Rashwood Worcs 58 D11
Raskelf N York 97 Q6
Rassau Blae G 30 G2
Rastrick Calder 90 E6
Ratagan Highld 145 R4
Ratby Leics 72 E9
Ratcliffe Culey Leics 72 A11
Ratcliffe on Soar Notts 72 D5
Ratcliffe on the Wreake Leics 72 G8
Rathen Abers 159 N5
Rathillet Fife 135 K3
Rathmell N York 96 B9
Ratho C Edin 127 L3
Ratho Station C Edin 127 L3
Rathven Moray 158 B4
Ratlake Hants 22 D10
Ratley Warwks 48 C5
Ratling Kent 39 M11
Ratlinghope Shrops 56 G5
Rattar Highld 167 N2
Ratten Row Cumb 101 K2
Ratten Row Cumb 110 G11
Ratten Row Lancs 88 E2
Rattery Devon 7 J6
Rattlesden Suffk 64 D10
Ratton Village E Susx 25 N10
Rattray P & K 142 B8
Raughton Cumb 110 G11
Raughton Head Cumb 110 G11
Raunds Nhants 61 L6
Ravenfield Rothm 91 M11
Ravenglass Cumb 100 E11
Ravenhills Green Worcs 46 D4
Raveningham Norfk 65 M2
Ravenscar N York 105 Q10
Ravenscraig N Lans 126 D6
Ravensdale IoM 80 e3
Ravensden Bed 61 N10
Ravenseat N York 102 G10
Ravenshead Notts 85 J10
Ravensmoor Ches E 69 R4
Ravensthorpe Kirk 90 G6
Ravensthorpe Nhants 60 E6
Ravenstone Leics 72 C8
Ravenstone M Keyn 49 M4
Ravenstonedale Cumb 102 D10
Ravenstruther S Lans 126 G8
Ravensworth N York 103 M9
Raw N York 105 P9
Rawcliffe C York 98 B10
Rawcliffe E R Yk 92 A6
Rawcliffe Bridge E R Yk 92 A6
Rawdon Leeds 90 G3
Rawling Street Kent 38 F10
Rawmarsh Rothm 91 L11
Rawnsley Staffs 58 F2
Rawreth Essex 38 C3
Rawridge Devon 10 E3
Rawtenstall Lancs 89 N6
Raydon Suffk 52 H4
Raylees Nthumb 112 D2
Rayleigh Essex 38 D3
Raymond's Hill Devon 10 G5
Rayne Essex 52 B7
Raynes Park Gt Lon 36 F7
Reach Cambs 63 J7
Read Lancs 89 M4
Reading Readg 35 K10
Reading Services W Berk 35 J11
Reading Street Kent 26 F5
Reading Street Kent 39 Q8
Reagill Cumb 102 B7
Rearquhar Highld 162 G8
Rearsby Leics 72 H8
Rease Heath Ches E 70 A4
Reawla Cnwll 2 G6
Reay Highld 166 G4
Reculver Kent 39 M8
Red Ball Devon 18 E11
Redberth Pembks 41 L10
Redbourn Herts 50 D8
Redbourne N Linc 92 G11
Redbrook Gloucs 31 P3
Redbrook Wrexhm 69 P6
Redbrook Street Kent 26 F4
Redburn Highld 156 G8
Redburn Nthumb 111 Q8
Redcar R & Cl 104 H6
Redcastle D & G 108 H7
Redcastle Highld 155 Q8
Red Dial Cumb 110 E11
Redding Falk 126 G2
Reddingmuirhead Falk 126 G2
Reddish Stockp 83 J6
Redditch Worcs 58 F11
Rede Suffk 63 P9
Redenhall Norfk 65 K5
Redenham Hants 22 B5
Redesmouth Nthumb 112 C4
Redford Abers 143 P3
Redford Angus 143 K9
Redford W Susx 23 N9
Redfordgreen Border 117 M7
Redgate Rhondd 30 D7
Redgorton P & K 134 D2
Redgrave Suffk 64 E6
Redhill Abers 151 K7
Red Hill BCP 13 J5
Redhill Herts 50 H4
Redhill N Som 19 N2
Redhill Surrey 36 G10
Red Hill Warwks 47 M3
Redisham Suffk 65 N5
Redland Bristl 31 Q9
Redland Ork 169 c4
Redlingfield Suffk 64 H7
Redlingfield Green Suffk 64 H7
Red Lodge Suffk 63 M6
Red Lumb Rochdl 89 N7
Redlynch Somset 20 D8
Redlynch Wilts 21 P10
Redmain Cumb 100 F4

290 Redmarley – Ruddle

Redmarley Worcs 57 P11
Redmarley D'Abitot Gloucs 46 E8
Redmarshall S on T 104 C6
Redmile Leics 73 K3
Redmire N York 96 F2
Redmyre Abers 143 P2
Rednal Birm 58 F9
Rednal Shrops 69 L9
Redpath Border 118 A3
Red Point Highld 153 N4
Red Post Cnwll 16 D10
Red Rice Hants 22 B6
Red Rock Wigan 88 H9
Red Roses Carmth 41 P8
Red Row Nthumb 119 Q11
Redruth Cnwll 2 H5
Redstocks Wilts 20 H2
Redstone P & K 142 B11
Redstone Cross Pembks 41 M7
Red Street Staffs 70 E4
Redvales Bury 89 N9
Red Wharf Bay IoA 79 J8
Redwick Newpt 31 M8
Redwick S Glos 31 P7
Redworth Darltn 103 P6
Reed Herts 51 J3
Reedham Norfk 77 N11
Reedness E R Yk 92 C6
Reeds Beck Lincs 86 H7
Reeds Holme Lancs 89 N6
Reepham Lincs 86 D6
Reepham Norfk 76 G7
Reeth N York 103 K11
Reeves Green Solhll 59 L9
Regaby IoM 80 f2
Regil N Som 19 P2
Reiff Highld 160 F4
Reigate Surrey 36 G10
Reighton N York 99 N5
Reinigeadal W Isls 168 h7
Reisque Abers 151 M4
Reiss Highld 167 P6
Rejerrah Cnwll 4 B10
Releath Cnwll 2 H7
Relubbus Cnwll 2 F7
Relugas Moray 156 H8
Remenham Wokham 35 L8
Remenham Hill Wokham 35 L8
Rempstone Notts 72 F6
Rendcomb Gloucs 33 K3
Rendham Suffk 65 L9
Rendlesham Suffk 65 L11
Renfrew Rens 125 N4
Renhold Bed 61 N10
Renishaw Derbys 84 G5
Rennington Nthumb 119 P7
Renton W Duns 125 K2
Renwick Cumb 101 Q2
Repps Norfk 77 N8
Repton Derbys 71 Q9
Reraig Highld 145 P2
Resaurie Highld 156 C8
Rescassa Cnwll 3 P5
Rescorla Cnwll 3 P4
Resipole Burn Highld 138 C5
Reskadinnick Cnwll 2 G5
Resolis Highld 156 B4
Resolven Neath 29 M4
Rest and be thankful Ag & B 131 Q6
Reston Border 129 M7
Restronguet Cnwll 3 L6
Reswallie Angus 143 J7
Reterth Cnwll 4 E9
Retford Notts 85 M4
Retire Cnwll 4 G9
Rettendon Common Essex 38 C2
Rettendon Village Essex 38 C2
Retyn Cnwll 4 D10
Revesby Lincs 87 J8
Rew Devon 7 J11
Rew Devon 7 K4
Rewe Devon 9 M5
Rew Street IoW 14 E8
Rexon Devon 5 Q4
Reydon Suffk 65 P6
Reymerston Norfk 76 E10
Reynalton Pembks 41 L9
Reynoldston Swans 28 E7
Rezare Cnwll 5 P6
Rhadyr Mons 31 L4
Rhandirmwyn Carmth 43 Q6
Rhayader Powys 55 M11
Rheindown Highld 155 P8
Rhenigidale W Isls 168 h7
Rhes-y-cae Flints 80 H10
Rhewl Denbgs 68 F2
Rhewl Denbgs 68 G6
Rhewl Mostyn Flints 80 H8
Rhicarn Highld 164 C11
Rhiconich Highld 164 G6
Rhicullen Highld 156 B3
Rhigos Rhondd 29 P3
Rhives Highld 163 J6
Rhiwbina Cardif 30 G8
Rhiwbryfdir Gwynd 67 M5
Rhiwderyn Newpt 31 J7
Rhiwen Gwynd 67 K2
Rhiwinder Rhondd 30 D7
Rhiwlas Gwynd 68 B7
Rhiwlas Gwynd 79 K11
Rhiwlas Powys 68 G8
Rhiwsaeson Rhondd 30 E8
Rhode Somset 19 J8
Rhoden Green Kent 37 Q11
Rhodesia Notts 85 J5
Rhodes Minnis Kent 27 L3
Rhodiad-y-brenin Pembks 40 E5
Rhonehouse D & G 108 F9
Rhoose V Glam 30 E11
Rhos Carmth 42 G7
Rhos Denbgs 68 F2
Rhos Neath 29 K4
Rhosaman Carmth 29 K2
Rhosbeirio IoA 78 F6
Rhoscefnhir IoA 79 J9
Rhoscolyn IoA 78 D9
Rhoscrowther Pembks 40 H10
Rhosesmor Flints 81 J11
Rhos-fawr Gwynd 66 F7
Rhosgadfan Gwynd 67 J3
Rhosgoch IoA 78 G7
Rhosgoch Powys 44 H5
Rhos Haminiog Cerdgn 43 K2
Rhoshill Pembks 41 N2
Rhoshirwaun Gwynd 66 C9
Rhoslan Gwynd 66 H6
Rhoslefain Gwynd 54 D3
Rhosllanerchrugog Wrexhm 69 J5
Rhôs Lligwy IoA 78 H7
Rhosmaen Carmth 43 M10
Rhosmeirch IoA 78 H9
Rhosneigr IoA 78 E10
Rhosnesni Wrexhm 69 L4
Rhôs-on-Sea Conwy 79 Q8
Rhosrobin Wrexhm 69 K4
Rhossili Swans 28 D7
Rhostrehwfa IoA 78 G10
Rhostryfan Gwynd 66 H3
Rhostyllen Wrexhm 69 K5
Rhosybol IoA 78 G7
Rhos-y-brithdir Powys 68 F10
Rhosygadfa Shrops 69 K8
Rhos-y-garth Cerdgn 54 E10
Rhos-y-gwaliau Gwynd 68 B8
Rhos-y-llan Gwynd 66 C7
Rhosymedre Wrexhm 69 J6
Rhos-y-meirch Powys 56 D11
Rhu Ag & B 132 B11
Rhualt Denbgs 80 F9
Rhubodach Ag & B 124 C3
Rhuddall Heath Ches W 69 Q2
Rhuddlan Cerdgn 43 J6
Rhuddlan Denbgs 80 E9
Rhue Highld 161 J7
Rhulen Powys 44 G5
Rhunahaorine Ag & B 123 M10
Rhyd Gwynd 67 L6
Rhydargaeau Carmth 42 H9
Rhydcymerau Carmth 43 L7
Rhydd Worcs 46 F5
Rhyd-Ddu Gwynd 67 K4
Rhydding Neath 29 K5
Rhydgaled Conwy 68 C2
Rhydlanfair Conwy 67 Q4
Rhydlewis Cerdgn 42 F5
Rhydlios Gwynd 66 B9
Rhydlydan Conwy 68 A4
Rhydowen Cerdgn 42 H5
Rhydroser Cerdgn 54 D11
Rhydspence Herefs 45 J5
Rhydtalog Flints 68 H4
Rhyd-uchaf Gwynd 68 B7
Rhyd-y-clafdy Gwynd 66 E8
Rhydycroesau Shrops 68 H8
Rhydyfelin Cerdgn 54 D9
Rhydyfelin Rhondd 30 E7
Rhyd-y-foel Conwy 80 C9
Rhydyfro Neath 29 K3
Rhyd-y-groes Gwynd 79 K11
Rhydymain Gwynd 67 Q10
Rhyd-y-meirch Mons 31 K3
Rhydymwyn Flints 81 J11
Rhyd-y-pennau Cerdgn 54 E7
Rhyd-yr-onnen Gwynd 54 E4
Rhyd-y-sarn Gwynd 67 M6
Rhyl Denbgs 80 E8
Rhymney Caerph 30 F3
Rhynd P & K 134 F3
Rhynie Abers 150 D2
Rhynie Highld 163 J11
Ribbesford Worcs 57 P10
Ribbleton Lancs 88 H4
Ribby Lancs 88 E4
Ribchester Lancs 89 K3
Riber Derbys 84 D9
Riby Lincs 93 L9
Riccall N York 91 Q3
Riccarton Border 111 K2
Riccarton E Ayrs 125 L10
Richards Castle Herefs 56 H11
Richings Park Bucks 36 B5
Richmond Gt Lon 36 E6
Richmond N York 103 N10
Richmond Sheff 84 F3
Rich's Holford Somset 18 F8
Rickerscote Staffs 70 G10
Rickford N Som 19 N3
Rickham Devon 7 K11
Rickinghall Suffk 64 E6
Rickling Essex 51 L4
Rickling Green Essex 51 M5
Rickmansworth Herts 36 C2
Riddell Border 117 Q6
Riddings Derbys 84 F10
Riddlecombe Devon 17 L9
Riddlesden C Brad 90 D2
Ridge BaNES 19 Q3
Ridge Dorset 12 F7
Ridge Herts 50 F10
Ridge Wilts 21 J8
Ridgebourne Powys 44 F2
Ridge Green Surrey 36 H11
Ridge Lane Warwks 59 L6
Ridge Row Kent 27 M3
Ridgeway Derbys 84 F4
Ridgeway Worcs 47 K2
Ridgeway Cross Herefs 46 D5
Ridgewell Essex 52 B3
Ridgewood E Susx 25 L7
Ridgmont C Beds 49 Q7
Riding Mill Nthumb 112 F8
Ridley Kent 37 P8
Ridley Nthumb 111 Q8
Ridley Green Ches E 69 Q4
Ridlington Norfk 77 L5
Ridlington Rutlnd 73 L10
Ridlington Street Norfk 77 L5
Ridsdale Nthumb 112 D4
Rievaulx N York 98 B3
Rigg D & G 110 E7
Riggend N Lans 126 D3
Righoul Highld 156 F7
Rigmadon Park Cumb 95 N4
Rigsby Lincs 87 M5
Rigside S Lans 116 B3
Riley Green Lancs 89 J5
Rileyhill Staffs 58 H2
Rilla Mill Cnwll 5 M7
Rillaton Cnwll 5 M7
Rillington N York 98 H6
Rimington Lancs 96 B11
Rimpton Somset 20 B10
Rimswell E R Yk 93 P5
Rinaston Pembks 41 J5
Rindleford Shrops 57 N5
Ringford D & G 108 E9
Ringinglow Sheff 84 C4
Ringland Norfk 76 G9
Ringles Cross E Susx 25 L6
Ringlestone Kent 38 E10
Ringley Bolton 89 M9
Ringmer E Susx 25 K8
Ringmore Devon 6 H9
Ringmore Devon 7 N4
Ringorm Moray 157 P9
Ring's End Cambs 74 G10
Ringsfield Suffk 65 N4
Ringsfield Corner Suffk 65 N4
Ringshall Herts 35 Q2
Ringshall Suffk 64 E11
Ringshall Stocks Suffk 64 F11
Ringstead Nhants 61 L5
Ringstead Norfk 75 P2
Ringwood Hants 13 L3
Ringwould Kent 27 Q2
Rinmore Abers 150 C4
Rinsey Cnwll 2 F8
Rinsey Croft Cnwll 2 G8
Ripe E Susx 25 M8
Ripley Derbys 84 E10
Ripley Hants 13 L5
Ripley N York 97 L8
Ripley Surrey 36 C9
Riplingham E R Yk 92 G4
Riplington Hants 23 J10
Ripon N York 97 M6
Rippingale Lincs 74 A5
Ripple Kent 39 Q11
Ripple Worcs 46 G7
Ripponden Calder 90 C7
Risabus Ag & B 122 D11
Risbury Herefs 45 Q4
Risby N Linc 92 F8
Risby Suffk 63 P7
Risca Caerph 30 H6
Rise E R Yk 93 L2
Riseden E Susx 25 P4
Riseden Kent 26 B4
Risegate Lincs 74 D5
Riseholme Lincs 86 C5
Risehow Cumb 100 D4
Riseley Bed 61 M8
Riseley Wokham 23 K2
Rishangles Suffk 64 H8
Rishton Lancs 89 L4
Rishworth Calder 90 C7
Rising Bridge Lancs 89 M5
Risley Derbys 72 D3
Risley Warrtn 82 E6
Risplith N York 97 K7
Rivar Wilts 22 B2
Rivenhall End Essex 52 D8
River Kent 27 N3
River W Susx 23 P10
River Bank Cambs 62 H7
Riverford Highld 155 P7
Riverhead Kent 37 M9
Rivers Corner Dorset 12 C2
Rivington Lancs 89 J8
Rivington Services Lancs 89 J8
Roachill Devon 17 R7
Roade Nhants 49 L4
Road Green Norfk 65 K3
Roadhead Cumb 111 K6
Roadmeetings S Lans 126 F8
Roadside E Ayrs 115 L4
Roadside Highld 167 L4
Roadwater Somset 18 D7
Roag Highld 152 D9
Roa Island Cumb 94 E7
Roan of Craigoch S Ayrs 114 E7
Roast Green Essex 51 L4
Roath Cardif 30 G9
Roberton Border 117 N8
Roberton S Lans 116 C5
Robertsbridge E Susx 26 B7
Roberttown Kirk 90 F6
Robeston Wathen Pembks 41 L7
Robgill Tower D & G 110 D6
Robin Hill Staffs 70 G3
Robin Hood Lancs 88 G8
Robin Hood Leeds 91 J5
Robinhood End Essex 52 B4
Robin Hood's Bay N York 105 Q9
Roborough Devon 6 E6
Roborough Devon 17 K8
Robroyston C Glas 125 Q4
Roby Knows 81 N6
Roby Mill Lancs 88 G9
Rocester Staffs 71 L7
Roch Pembks 40 G6
Rochdale Rochdl 89 P8
Roche Cnwll 4 F9
Rochester Medway 38 B8
Rochester Nthumb 118 F11
Rochford Essex 38 E3
Rochford Worcs 57 L11
Roch Gate Pembks 40 G6
Rock Cnwll 4 E6
Rock Neath 29 L6
Rock Nthumb 119 P6
Rock W Susx 24 D8
Rock Worcs 57 N10
Rockbeare Devon 9 P6
Rockbourne Hants 21 M11
Rockcliffe Cumb 110 G8
Rockcliffe D & G 108 H10
Rockcliffe Cross Cumb 110 F8
Rock End Staffs 70 F3
Rockend Torbay 7 N6
Rock Ferry Wirral 81 L7
Rockfield Highld 163 L10
Rockfield Mons 31 N2
Rockford Devon 17 P2
Rockford Hants 13 L3
Rockgreen Shrops 57 J9
Rockhampton S Glos 32 C6
Rockhead Cnwll 4 H5
Rockhill Shrops 56 D9
Rock Hill Worcs 58 E11
Rockingham Nhants 61 J2
Rockland All Saints Norfk 64 D2
Rockland St Mary Norfk 77 L11
Rockland St Peter Norfk 64 D2
Rockley Notts 85 M6
Rockley Wilts 33 N10
Rockliffe Lancs 89 P6
Rockville Ag & B 131 Q9
Rockwell End Bucks 35 L7
Rockwell Green Somset 18 F10
Rodborough Gloucs 32 F4
Rodbourne Swindn 33 M7
Rodbourne Wilts 32 H8
Rodd Herefs 45 L2
Roddam Nthumb 119 K6
Rodden Dorset 11 N8
Roddymoor Dur 103 N3
Rode Somset 20 F4
Rode Heath Ches E 70 E3
Rode Heath Ches E 83 J11
Rodel W Isls 168 f9
Roden Wrekin 69 Q11
Rodhuish Somset 18 D7
Rodington Wrekin 57 K2
Rodington Heath Wrekin 57 K2
Rodley Gloucs 32 D2
Rodley Leeds 90 G3
Rodmarton Gloucs 32 H5
Rodmell E Susx 25 K9
Rodmersham Kent 38 F9
Rodmersham Green Kent 38 F9
Rodney Stoke Somset 19 N5
Rodsley Derbys 71 N6
Rodway Somset 19 J6
Roecliffe N York 97 N7
Roe Cross Tamesd 83 L5
Roe Green Herts 50 F9
Roe Green Herts 50 H4
Roe Green Salfd 82 F4
Roehampton Gt Lon 36 F6
Roffey W Susx 24 E4
Rogart Highld 162 G6
Rogate W Susx 23 M10
Roger Ground Cumb 101 L11
Rogerstone Newpt 31 J7
Roghadal W Isls 168 f9
Rogiet Mons 31 N7
Roke Oxon 34 H6
Roker Sundld 113 P9
Rollesby Norfk 77 N8
Rolleston Leics 73 J10
Rolleston Notts 85 M10
Rollestone Wilts 21 L5
Rolleston on Dove Staffs 71 N9
Rolston E R Yk 93 M2
Rolstone N Som 19 L2
Rolvenden Kent 26 D5
Rolvenden Layne Kent 26 E5
Romaldkirk Dur 103 J6
Romanby N York 97 N2
Romanno Bridge Border 127 M8
Romansleigh Devon 17 N7
Romden Castle Kent 26 E3
Romesdal Highld 152 G7
Romford Dorset 13 J3
Romford Gt Lon 37 M3
Romiley Stockp 83 K6
Romney Street Kent 37 N8
Romsey Cambs 62 G9
Romsey Hants 22 C10
Romsley Shrops 57 P8
Romsley Worcs 58 E8
Rona Highld 153 L6
Ronachan Ag & B 123 M9
Rood Ashton Wilts 20 G3
Rookhope Dur 102 H2
Rookley IoW 14 F10
Rookley Green IoW 14 F10
Rooks Bridge Somset 19 L4
Rooks Nest Somset 18 E8
Rookwith N York 97 K3
Roos E R Yk 93 N4
Roose Cumb 94 E7
Roosebeck Cumb 94 F7
Roothams Green Bed 61 N9
Ropley Hants 22 H8
Ropley Dean Hants 22 H8
Ropley Soke Hants 23 J8
Ropsley Lincs 73 P4
Rora Abers 159 Q7
Rorrington Shrops 56 E4
Rosarie Moray 158 A7
Rose Cnwll 3 K3
Roseacre Lancs 88 E3
Rose Ash Devon 17 P7
Rosebank S Lans 126 E8
Rosebush Pembks 41 L5
Rosecare Cnwll 5 K2
Rosecliston Cnwll 4 C10
Rosedale Abbey N York 105 K11
Rose Green Essex 52 F6
Rose Green Suffk 52 F4
Rose Green Suffk 52 G3
Rose Green W Susx 15 P7
Rosehall Highld 162 B6
Rosehearty Abers 159 M4
Rose Hill E Susx 25 L7
Rose Hill Lancs 89 N4
Rosehill Shrops 69 N11
Roseisle Moray 157 L4
Roselands E Susx 25 P10
Rosemarket Pembks 41 J9
Rosemarkie Highld 156 C6
Rosemary Lane Devon 10 D2
Rosemount P & K 142 B9
Rosenannon Cnwll 4 F8
Rosenithon Cnwll 3 L9
Roser's Cross E Susx 25 M6
Rosevean Cnwll 4 G10
Rosevine Cnwll 3 M6
Rosewarne Cnwll 2 G6
Rosewell Mdloth 127 P5
Roseworth S on T 104 D6
Roseworthy Cnwll 2 G6
Rosgill Cumb 101 P7
Roskestal Cnwll 2 B9
Roskhill Highld 152 D9
Roskorwell Cnwll 3 K9
Rosley Cumb 110 F11
Roslin Mdloth 127 P5
Rosliston Derbys 71 N11
Rosneath Ag & B 132 B11
Ross D & G 108 D12
Ross Nthumb 119 M3
Rossett Wrexhm 69 L3
Rossett Green N York 97 L10
Rossington Donc 91 Q11
Ross-on-Wye Herefs 46 A10
Roster Highld 167 N9
Rostherne Ches E 82 F8
Rosthwaite Cumb 101 J8
Roston Derbys 71 L6
Rosudgeon Cnwll 2 F8
Rosyth Fife 134 E11
Rothbury Nthumb 119 L10
Rotherby Leics 72 H7
Rotherfield E Susx 25 N5
Rotherfield Greys Oxon 35 K8
Rotherfield Peppard Oxon 35 K8
Rotherham Rothm 84 F2
Rothersthorpe Nhants 60 F9
Rotherwick Hants 23 K3
Rothes Moray 157 P8
Rothesay Ag & B 124 D5
Rothiebrisbane Abers 158 H10
Rothiemurchus Lodge Highld 148 H6
Rothienorman Abers 158 H10
Rothley Leics 72 F8
Rothley Nthumb 112 F3
Rothmaise Abers 158 G11
Rothwell Leeds 91 J5
Rothwell Lincs 93 K11
Rothwell Nhants 60 H4
Rotsea E R Yk 99 M10
Rottal Lodge Angus 142 F4
Rottingdean Br & H 25 J10
Rottington Cumb 100 C8
Roucan D & G 109 M5
Roud IoW 14 F10
Rougham Norfk 76 A7
Rougham Suffk 64 C9
Rough Close Staffs 70 G7
Rough Common Kent 39 K10
Roughlee Lancs 89 N2
Roughpark Abers 149 Q5
Roughton Lincs 86 H8
Roughton Norfk 77 J4
Roughton Shrops 57 P6
Roughway Kent 37 P10
Roundbush Essex 52 E11
Round Bush Herts 50 D11
Roundbush Green Essex 51 N8
Round Green Luton 50 D6
Roundham Somset 11 J3
Roundhay Leeds 91 J3
Rounds Green Sandw 58 E7
Round Street Kent 37 Q7
Roundstreet Common W Susx 24 C5
Roundswell Devon 17 J5
Roundway Wilts 21 K2
Roundyhill Angus 142 F7
Rousay Ork 169 c3
Rousdon Devon 10 F6
Rousham Oxon 48 E10
Rous Lench Worcs 47 K4
Routenburn N Ayrs 124 F5
Routh E R Yk 93 J2
Rout's Green Bucks 35 L5
Row Cnwll 4 H6
Row Cumb 95 K3
Row Cumb 102 B4
Rowanburn D & G 110 H5
Rowardennan Stirlg 132 D8
Rowarth Derbys 83 M7
Row Ash Hants 14 F4
Rowberrow Somset 19 N3
Rowborough IoW 14 E10
Rowde Wilts 21 J2
Rowden Devon 8 F5
Rowen Conwy 79 P10
Rowfield Derbys 71 M5
Rowfoot Nthumb 111 N8
Rowford Somset 18 H9
Row Green Essex 52 B7
Rowhedge Essex 52 H7
Rowhook W Susx 24 D4
Rowington Warwks 59 K11
Rowland Derbys 84 B6
Rowland's Castle Hants 15 K4
Rowlands Gill Gatesd 113 J9
Rowledge Surrey 23 M6
Rowley Dur 112 G11
Rowley E R Yk 92 G4
Rowley Shrops 56 E3
Rowley Hill Kirk 90 F8
Rowley Regis Sandw 58 E7
Rowlstone Herefs 45 M9
Rowly Surrey 24 B2
Rowner Hants 14 G6
Rowney Green Worcs 58 F10
Rownhams Hants 22 C11
Rownhams Services Hants 22 C11
Rowrah Cumb 100 E7
Rowsham Bucks 49 M11
Rowsley Derbys 84 C7
Rowstock Oxon 34 E7
Rowston Lincs 86 E9
Rowthorne Derbys 84 G8
Rowton Ches W 69 M2
Rowton Shrops 56 F2
Rowton Shrops 56 G8
Rowton Wrekin 69 R11
Row Town Surrey 36 B8
Roxburgh Border 118 C4
Roxby N Linc 92 F7
Roxby N York 105 L7
Roxton Bed 61 Q10
Roxwell Essex 51 P9
Royal Leamington Spa Warwks 59 M11
Royal Oak Darltn 103 P6
Royal Oak Lancs 81 N4
Royal's Green Ches E 69 R6
Royal Sutton Coldfield Birm 58 H5
Royal Tunbridge Wells Kent 25 N3
Royal Wootton Bassett Wilts 33 L8
Royal Yacht Britannia C Edin 127 P2
Roy Bridge Highld 146 H11
Roydhouse Kirk 90 G8
Roydon Essex 51 K8
Roydon Norfk 64 G5
Roydon Norfk 75 P6
Roydon Hamlet Essex 51 K9
Royston Barns 91 K8
Royston Herts 51 J2
Royton Oldham 89 Q9
Rozel Jersey 11 c1
Ruabon Wrexhm 69 K6
Ruaig Ag & B 136 D6
Ruan High Lanes Cnwll 3 N6
Ruan Lanihorne Cnwll 3 M5
Ruan Major Cnwll 3 J10
Ruan Minor Cnwll 3 J10
Ruardean Gloucs 46 B11
Ruardean Hill Gloucs 46 B11
Ruardean Woodside Gloucs 46 B11
Rubery Birm 58 E9
Rubha Ban W Isls 168 c16
Ruckcroft Cumb 101 P2
Ruckhall Herefs 45 P7
Ruckinge Kent 26 H5
Ruckland Lincs 87 K5
Ruckley Shrops 57 J4
Rudbaxton Pembks 41 J6
Rudby N York 104 E9
Rudchester Nthumb 112 H7
Ruddington Notts 72 F4
Ruddle Gloucs 32 C2

Ruddlemoor Cnwll	3	Q3
Rudford Gloucs	46	E10
Rudge Somset	20	F4
Rudgeway S Glos	32	B7
Rudgwick W Susx	24	C4
Rudhall Herefs	46	B9
Rudheath Ches W	82	E10
Rudheath Woods Ches E	82	F10
Rudley Green Essex	52	D11
Rudloe Wilts	32	F10
Rudry Caerph	30	H7
Rudston E R Yk	99	M7
Rudyard Staffs	70	H3
Ruecastle Border	118	B6
Rufford Lancs	88	F7
Rufford Abbey Notts	85	K8
Rufforth C York	98	A10
Rug Denbgs	68	E6
Rugby Warwks	60	B5
Rugby Services Warwks	60	B5
Rugeley Staffs	71	J11
Ruigh'riabhach Highld	160	G7
Ruisgarry W Isls	168	e9
Ruishton Somset	19	J9
Ruisigearraidh W Isls	168	e9
Ruislip Gt Lon	36	C3
Rùm Highld	144	E8
Rumbach Moray	158	A7
Rumbling Bridge P & K	134	C8
Rumburgh Suffk	65	L5
Rumby Hill Dur	103	N4
Rumford Cnwll	4	D7
Rumford Falk	126	G2
Rumney Cardif	30	H9
Rumwell Somset	18	G10
Runcorn Halton	81	Q8
Runcton W Susx	15	N6
Runcton Holme Norfk	75	M9
Runfold Surrey	23	N5
Runhall Norfk	76	F10
Runham Norfk	77	P9
Runham Norfk	77	Q10
Runnington Somset	18	F10
Runsell Green Essex	52	C10
Runshaw Moor Lancs	88	G7
Runswick N York	105	M7
Runtaleave Angus	142	D4
Runwell Essex	38	C3
Ruscombe Wokham	35	L9
Rushall Herefs	46	B7
Rushall Norfk	64	H5
Rushall Wilts	21	M3
Rushall Wsall	58	F4
Rushbrooke Suffk	64	B9
Rushbury Shrops	57	J6
Rushden Herts	50	H4
Rushden Nhants	61	L7
Rushenden Kent	38	F7
Rusher's Cross E Susx	25	P5
Rushford Devon	8	C9
Rushford Norfk	64	C5
Rush Green Essex	53	L8
Rush Green Gt Lon	37	M3
Rush Green Herts	50	F6
Rush Green Warrtn	82	E7
Rushlake Green E Susx	25	P7
Rushmere Suffk	65	P4
Rushmere St Andrew Suffk	53	L2
Rushmoor Surrey	23	N6
Rushock Herefs	45	L3
Rushock Worcs	58	C10
Rusholme Manch	83	J6
Rushton Ches W	69	Q2
Rushton Nhants	60	H4
Rushton Shrops	57	L3
Rushton Spencer Staffs	70	G2
Rushwick Worcs	46	F4
Rushyford Dur	103	Q5
Ruskie Stirlg	133	J7
Ruskington Lincs	86	E10
Rusland Cross Cumb	94	G3
Rusper W Susx	24	F3
Ruspidge Gloucs	32	C2
Russell Green Essex	52	B9
Russell's Water Oxon	35	K7
Russel's Green Suffk	65	K7
Russ Hill Surrey	24	F2
Rusthall Kent	25	N3
Rustington W Susx	24	B10
Ruston N York	99	K4
Ruston Parva E R Yk	99	M8
Ruswarp N York	105	N9
Ruthall Shrops	57	K6
Rutherford Border	118	B4
Rutherglen S Lans	125	Q5
Ruthernbridge Cnwll	4	G8
Ruthin Denbgs	68	F3
Ruthrieston C Aber	151	N7
Ruthven Abers	158	D8
Ruthven Angus	142	D8
Ruthven Highld	148	D8
Ruthven Highld	156	E11
Ruthvoes Cnwll	4	E9
Ruthwaite Cumb	100	H3
Ruthwell D & G	109	N7
Ruxley Gt Lon	37	L6
Ruxton Green Herefs	45	Q11
Ruyton-XI-Towns Shrops	69	L10
Ryal Nthumb	112	F6
Ryall Dorset	11	J5
Ryall Worcs	46	G6
Ryarsh Kent	37	Q8
Rycote Oxon	35	J3
Rydal Cumb	101	L9
Ryde IoW	14	G8
Rye E Susx	26	F7
Ryebank Shrops	69	P8
Ryeford Herefs	46	B10
Rye Foreign E Susx	26	E7
Rye Harbour E Susx	26	F8
Ryehill E R Yk	93	M5
Ryeish Green Wokham	35	K11
Rye Street Worcs	46	E7
Ryhall Rutlnd	73	Q8
Ryhill Wakefd	91	K8
Ryhope Sundld	113	P10
Rylah Derbys	84	G7
Ryland Lincs	86	D5
Rylands Notts	72	E3
Rylstone N York	96	E9
Ryme Intrinseca Dorset	11	M2
Ryther N York	91	P3
Ryton Gatesd	113	J8
Ryton N York	98	F5
Ryton Shrops	57	P4
Ryton Warwks	59	P9

Ryton-on-Dunsmore Warwks	59	N10
Ryton Woodside Gatesd	112	H8
RZSS Edinburgh Zoo C Edin	127	N3

S

Sabden Lancs	89	M3
Sabine's Green Essex	51	M11
Sacombe Herts	50	H7
Sacombe Green Herts	50	H7
Sacriston Dur	113	K11
Sadberge Darltn	104	B7
Saddell Ag & B	120	E5
Saddington Leics	60	E2
Saddle Bow Norfk	75	M7
Saddlescombe W Susx	24	G8
Sadgill Cumb	101	N9
Saffron Walden Essex	51	M3
Sageston Pembks	41	L10
Saham Hills Norfk	76	C11
Saham Toney Norfk	76	B11
Saighton Ches W	69	M2
St Abbs Border	129	N6
St Agnes Border	128	H7
St Agnes Cnwll	3	J3
St Agnes IoS	2	b3
St Agnes Mining District Cnwll	3	J4
St Albans Herts	50	D9
St Allen Cnwll	3	L3
St Andrew Guern	10	b2
St Andrews Fife	135	N4
St Andrews Botanic Garden Fife	135	N4
St Andrews Major V Glam	30	F10
St Andrews Well Dorset	11	K6
St Anne's Lancs	88	C5
St Ann's D & G	109	N2
St Ann's Chapel Cnwll	5	Q7
St Ann's Chapel Devon	6	H9
St Anthony-in-Meneage Cnwll	3	K8
St Anthony's Hill E Susx	25	P10
St Arvans Mons	31	P5
St Asaph Denbgs	80	E10
St Athan V Glam	30	D11
St Aubin Jersey	11	b2
St Austell Cnwll	3	Q3
St Bees Cumb	100	C8
St Blazey Cnwll	3	R3
St Blazey Gate Cnwll	3	R3
St Boswells Border	118	A4
St Brelade Jersey	11	a2
St Brelade's Bay Jersey	11	a2
St Breock Cnwll	4	F7
St Breward Cnwll	4	H6
St Briavels Gloucs	31	Q4
St Brides Pembks	40	F8
St Brides Major V Glam	29	N10
St Brides Netherwent Mons	31	M7
St Brides-super-Ely V Glam	30	E9
St Brides Wentlooge Newpt	31	J8
St Budeaux C Plym	6	D7
Saintbury Gloucs	47	M7
St Buryan Cnwll	2	C8
St Catherine BaNES	32	E11
St Catherines Ag & B	131	N6
St Chloe Gloucs	32	F4
St Clears Carmth	41	Q7
St Cleer Cnwll	5	L8
St Clement Cnwll	3	M5
St Clement Jersey	11	c2
St Clether Cnwll	5	L5
St Colmac Ag & B	124	C4
St Columb Major Cnwll	4	E9
St Columb Minor Cnwll	4	C9
St Columb Road Cnwll	4	E10
St Combs Abers	159	Q5
St Cross South Elmham Suffk	65	K5
St Cyrus Abers	143	N5
St David's P & K	133	Q3
St Davids Pembks	40	E5
St Davids Cathedral Pembks	40	E5
St Day Cnwll	3	J5
St Decumans Somset	18	E6
St Dennis Cnwll	4	F10
St Devereux Herefs	45	N8
St Dogmaels Pembks	42	C5
St Dogwells Pembks	41	J5
St Dominick Cnwll	5	Q8
St Donats V Glam	29	P11
St Edith's Marsh Wilts	21	J2
St Endellion Cnwll	4	F6
St Enoder Cnwll	4	D10
St Erme Cnwll	3	L4
St Erney Cnwll	5	P10
St Erth Cnwll	2	F6
St Erth Praze Cnwll	2	F6
St Ervan Cnwll	4	D7
St Eval Cnwll	4	D8
St Ewe Cnwll	3	P4
St Fagans Cardif	30	F9
St Fagans: National History Museum Cardif	30	F9
St Fergus Abers	159	Q7
St Fillans P & K	133	K3
St Florence Pembks	41	L10
St Gennys Cnwll	5	J2
St George Conwy	80	D9
St Georges N Som	19	L2
St George's V Glam	30	F9
St George's Hill Surrey	36	C8
St Germans Cnwll	5	P10
St Giles in the Wood Devon	17	J8
St Giles-on-the-Heath Devon	5	P3
St Gluvia's Cnwll	3	K7
St Harmon Powys	55	M10
St Helen Auckland Dur	103	N5
St Helens Cnwll	100	D4
St Helen's E Susx	26	D9
St Helens IoW	14	H9
St Helens St Hel	81	Q5
St Helier Gt Lon	36	G7
St Helier Jersey	11	b2
St Hilary Cnwll	2	E7
St Hilary V Glam	30	D10
Saint Hill Devon	10	B3
Saint Hill W Susx	25	J3
St Illtyd Blae G	30	H4
St Ippolyts Herts	50	E5
St Ishmael's Pembks	40	F9

St Issey Cnwll	4	E7
St Ive Cnwll	5	N8
St Ive Cross Cnwll	5	N8
St Ives Cambs	62	D6
St Ives Cnwll	2	E5
St Ives Dorset	13	K4
St James Norfk	77	K7
St James's End Nhants	60	F8
St James South Elmham Suffk	65	L5
St Jidgey Cnwll	4	E8
St John Cnwll	5	Q11
St John Jersey	11	b1
St Johns Dur	103	L4
St John's E Susx	25	M4
St John's IoM	80	c5
St John's Kent	37	M9
St Johns Surrey	23	Q3
St Johns Worcs	46	F4
St John's Chapel Devon	17	J6
St John's Chapel Dur	102	G3
St John's Fen End Norfk	75	K8
St John's Highway Norfk	75	K8
St John's Kirk S Lans	116	D3
St John's Town of Dalry D & G	108	D4
St John's Wood Gt Lon	36	G4
St Judes IoM	80	e2
St Just-in-Roseland Cnwll	3	L6
St Just Mining District Cnwll	2	B7
St Katherines Abers	159	J11
St Keverne Cnwll	3	K9
St Kew Cnwll	4	G6
St Kew Highway Cnwll	4	G6
St Keyne Cnwll	5	L9
St Lawrence Cnwll	4	G8
St Lawrence Essex	52	G11
St Lawrence IoW	14	F11
St Lawrence Jersey	11	b1
St Lawrence Kent	39	Q8
St Leonards Bucks	35	P3
St Leonards Dorset	13	K4
St Leonards E Susx	26	D10
St Leonard's Street Kent	37	Q9
St Levan Cnwll	2	B9
St Luke's Park Essex	38	C2
St Lythans V Glam	30	F10
St Mabyn Cnwll	4	G7
St Madoes P & K	134	F3
St Margarets Herefs	45	M8
St Margarets Herts	51	J8
St Margaret's at Cliffe Kent	27	Q3
St Margaret's Hope Ork	169	d7
St Margaret South Elmham Suffk	65	L5
St Marks IoM	80	c7
St Martin Cnwll	3	K9
St Martin Cnwll	5	M10
St Martin Guern	10	b2
St Martin Jersey	11	c1
St Martin's IoS	2	c1
St Martin's P & K	142	B11
St Martin's Shrops	69	K7
St Martin's Moor Shrops	69	K7
St Mary Jersey	11	a1
St Mary Bourne Hants	22	D4
St Marychurch Torbay	7	N5
St Mary Church V Glam	30	D10
St Mary Cray Gt Lon	37	L7
St Mary Hill V Glam	30	C9
St Mary in the Marsh Kent	27	J6
St Mary's IoS	2	c2
St Mary's Ork	169	d6
St Mary's Bay Kent	27	J6
St Mary's Hoo Medway	38	D6
St Mary's Platt Kent	37	P9
St Maughans Mons	45	P11
St Maughans Green Mons	45	P11
St Mawes Cnwll	3	L7
St Mawgan Cnwll	4	D8
St Mellion Cnwll	5	P8
St Mellons Cardif	30	H8
St Merryn Cnwll	4	D7
St Mewan Cnwll	3	P3
St Michael Caerhays Cnwll	3	P5
St Michael Church Somset	19	K8
St Michael Penkevil Cnwll	3	M5
St Michaels Kent	26	E4
St Michaels Worcs	57	K11
St Michael's Mount Cnwll	2	E8
St Michael's on Wyre Lancs	88	F2
St Michael South Elmham Suffk	65	L5
St Minver Cnwll	4	F6
St Monans Fife	135	N7
St Neot Cnwll	5	K8
St Neots Cambs	61	Q8
St Newlyn East Cnwll	4	C10
St Nicholas Pembks	40	H3
St Nicholas V Glam	30	E10
St Nicholas-at-Wade Kent	39	N8
St Ninians Stirlg	133	M9
St Olaves Norfk	65	P2
St Osyth Essex	53	K8
St Ouen Jersey	11	a1
St Owen's Cross Herefs	45	Q10
St Paul's Cray Gt Lon	37	L7
St Paul's Walden Herts	50	E6
St Peter Jersey	11	a1
St Peter Port Guern	10	c2
St Peter's Guern	10	b2
St Peter's Kent	39	Q8
St Peter's Hill Cambs	62	B6
St Petrox Pembks	41	J11
St Pinnock Cnwll	5	L9
St Quivox S Ayrs	114	G3
St Ruan Cnwll	3	J10
St Sampson Cnwll	3	c1
St Saviour Guern	10	b2
St Saviour Jersey	11	b2
St Stephen Cnwll	3	N3
St Stephens Cnwll	5	N4
St Stephens Cnwll	5	Q10
St Teath Cnwll	4	H5
St Thomas Devon	9	M6
St Margaret's Bay Kent	27	Q3
St Tudy Cnwll	4	H6
St Twynnells Pembks	41	J11
St Veep Cnwll	5	J10
St Vigeans Angus	143	L9
St Wenn Cnwll	4	F9
St Weonards Herefs	45	P10
St Winnow Cnwll	5	J10
St y-Nyll V Glam	30	E9

Salcombe Devon	7	J11
Salcombe Regis Devon	10	D7
Salcott-cum-Virley Essex	52	F9
Sale Traffd	82	G6
Saleby Lincs	87	N5
Sale Green Worcs	46	H3
Salehurst E Susx	26	C7
Salem Carmth	43	M9
Salem Gwynd	54	F8
Salen Ag & B	137	P7
Salen Highld	138	B5
Salesbury Lancs	89	K4
Salford C Beds	49	P7
Salford Oxon	47	Q9
Salford Salfd	82	H5
Salford Priors Warwks	47	L4
Salfords Surrey	36	G11
Salhouse Norfk	77	L9
Saline Fife	134	C9
Salisbury Wilts	21	M8
Salisbury Plain Wilts	21	L6
Salkeld Dykes Cumb	101	P3
Sallachy Highld	162	C5
Salle Norfk	76	G7
Salmonby Lincs	87	K6
Salperton Gloucs	47	L10
Salph End Bed	61	N10
Salsburgh N Lans	126	E5
Salt Staffs	70	H9
Salta Cumb	109	N11
Saltaire C Brad	90	E3
Saltaire C Brad	90	E3
Saltash Cnwll	6	C7
Saltburn Highld	156	C3
Saltburn-by-the-Sea R & Cl	105	J6
Saltby Leics	73	M5
Salt Coates Cumb	110	C10
Saltcoats Cumb	100	E11
Saltcoats N Ayrs	124	G9
Saltcotes Lancs	88	D5
Saltdean Br & H	25	J10
Salterbeck Cumb	100	C5
Salterforth Lancs	96	C11
Salterswall Ches W	82	D11
Salterton Wilts	21	M7
Saltfleet Lincs	87	N2
Saltfleetby All Saints Lincs	87	N2
Saltfleetby St Clement Lincs	87	N2
Saltfleetby St Peter Lincs	87	M3
Salford BaNES	32	C11
Salthouse Norfk	76	F3
Saltley Birm	58	H7
Saltmarsh Newpt	31	K8
Saltmarshe E R Yk	92	C6
Saltney Flints	69	L2
Salton N York	98	E5
Saltrens Devon	16	H7
Saltwick Nthumb	113	J4
Saltwood Kent	27	L4
Salvington W Susx	24	D9
Salwarpe Worcs	46	G2
Salway Ash Dorset	11	K5
Sambourne Warwks	47	L2
Sambrook Wrekin	70	C10
Samlesbury Lancs	88	H4
Samlesbury Bottoms Lancs	89	J5
Sampford Arundel Somset	18	F11
Sampford Brett Somset	18	E6
Sampford Courtenay Devon	8	F4
Sampford Moor Somset	18	F11
Sampford Peverell Devon	9	P2
Sampford Spiney Devon	6	E4
Samsonlane Ork	169	f4
Samson's Corner Essex	53	J8
Samuelston E Loth	128	D5
Sanaigmore Ag & B	122	B5
Sancreed Cnwll	2	C8
Sancton E R Yk	92	E3
Sand Somset	19	M5
Sandaig Highld	145	M7
Sandale Cumb	100	H2
Sandal Magna Wakefd	91	J7
Sandavore Highld	144	E11
Sanday Airport Ork	169	f2
Sandbach Ches E	70	D2
Sandbach Services Ches E	70	D2
Sandbank Ag & B	131	P11
Sandbanks BCP	12	H7
Sandend Abers	158	E4
Sanderstead Gt Lon	36	H8
Sandford Devon	9	K4
Sandford Dorset	12	D7
Sandford Hants	13	L4
Sandford IoW	14	F10
Sandford N Som	19	M3
Sandford S Lans	126	C9
Sandford Shrops	69	K10
Sandford Shrops	69	Q8
Sandford-on-Thames Oxon	34	F4
Sandford Orcas Dorset	20	B10
Sandford St Martin Oxon	48	D9
Sandgate Kent	27	M4
Sandhaven Abers	159	N4
Sandhead D & G	106	D8
Sandhill Rothm	91	L11
Sandhills Dorset	11	M4
Sandhills Dorset	11	P2
Sand Hills Leeds	91	K3
Sandhills Oxon	34	G3
Sandhills Surrey	23	P7
Sandhoe Nthumb	112	F7
Sandhole Ag & B	131	L8
Sand Hole E R Yk	92	D3
Sandholme E R Yk	92	D4
Sandholme Lincs	74	F3
Sandhurst Br For	23	M2
Sandhurst Gloucs	46	F10
Sandhurst Kent	26	D6
Sandhurst Cross Kent	26	C6
Sand Hutton N York	97	N4
Sandhutton N York	97	P4
Sandiacre Derbys	72	D3
Sandilands Lincs	87	P4
Sandiway Ches W	82	D10
Sandleheath Hants	21	M11
Sandleigh Oxon	34	E4
Sandley Dorset	20	E10
Sandling Kent	38	C10
Sandlow Green Ches E	82	G11
Sandness Shet	169	m8
Sandon Essex	52	B11
Sandon Herts	50	H4
Sandon Staffs	70	H8
Sandon Bank Staffs	70	G9
Sandown IoW	14	G10

Sandplace Cnwll	5	M10
Sandridge Herts	50	E8
Sandridge Wilts	32	H11
Sandringham Norfk	75	N5
Sands Bucks	35	M6
Sandsend N York	105	N8
Sand Side Cumb	94	E4
Sandside Cumb	95	K4
Sandtoft N Linc	92	B9
Sandway Kent	38	E11
Sandwich Kent	39	P10
Sandwich Bay Kent	39	Q10
Sandwick Cumb	101	M7
Sandwick Shet	169	r11
Sandwick W Isls	168	j4
Sandwith Cumb	100	C8
Sandwith Newtown Cumb	100	C8
Sandy C Beds	61	Q11
Sandy Bank Lincs	87	J9
Sandycroft Flints	81	L11
Sandy Cross E Susx	25	N6
Sandy Cross Herefs	46	C3
Sandyford D & G	110	D2
Sandygate Devon	7	M4
Sandygate IoM	80	e2
Sandy Haven Pembks	40	G9
Sandyhills D & G	109	J9
Sandylands Lancs	95	J8
Sandy Lane C Brad	90	E3
Sandylane Staffs	70	C7
Sandylane Swans	28	G7
Sandy Lane Wilts	33	J11
Sandy Lane Wrexhm	69	M6
Sandy Park Devon	8	G7
Sandysike Cumb	110	G7
Sandyway Herefs	45	P9
Sangobeg Highld	165	K3
Sangomore Highld	165	K3
Sankey Bridges Warrtn	82	C7
Sankyn's Green Worcs	57	P11
Sanna Highld	137	L2
Sanndabhaig W Isls	168	j4
Sannox N Ayrs	124	C8
Sanquhar D & G	115	Q6
Santon Cumb	100	F10
Santon IoM	80	d7
Santon Bridge Cumb	100	F10
Santon Downham Suffk	63	P3
Sapcote Leics	59	Q6
Sapey Common Herefs	46	D2
Sapiston Suffk	64	C6
Sapley Cambs	62	B6
Sapperton Derbys	71	M8
Sapperton Gloucs	32	H4
Sapperton Lincs	73	Q4
Saracen's Head Lincs	74	F5
Sarclet Highld	167	P8
Sarisbury Hants	14	F5
Sarn Brdgnd	29	P8
Sarn Powys	56	C6
Sarnau Carmth	42	F11
Sarnau Cerdgn	42	F5
Sarnau Gwynd	68	C7
Sarnau Powys	44	E8
Sarnau Powys	68	H11
Sarn Bach Gwynd	66	E9
Sarnesfield Herefs	45	M4
Sarn Mellteyrn Gwynd	66	C8
Sarn Park Services Brdgnd	29	P8
Sarn-wen Powys	69	J11
Saron Carmth	28	H2
Saron Carmth	42	G7
Saron Gwynd	66	H3
Saron Gwynd	79	J11
Sarratt Herts	50	B11
Sarre Kent	39	N8
Sarsden Oxon	47	Q10
Sarson Hants	22	B6
Satley Dur	103	M2
Satmar Kent	27	N4
Satron N York	102	H11
Satterleigh Devon	17	M7
Satterthwaite Cumb	94	G2
Satwell Oxon	35	K8
Sauchen Abers	151	J5
Saucher P & K	142	B11
Sauchieburn Abers	143	M4
Saul Gloucs	32	D3
Saundby Notts	85	N3
Saundersfoot Pembks	41	M10
Saunderton Bucks	35	L4
Saunderton Station Bucks	35	M5
Saunton Devon	16	H4
Sausthorpe Lincs	87	L7
Saverley Green Staffs	70	H7
Savile Town Kirk	90	G6
Sawbridge Warwks	60	B7
Sawbridgeworth Herts	51	L8
Sawdon N York	99	J4
Sawley Derbys	72	D4
Sawley Lancs	96	A11
Sawley N York	97	K7
Sawston Cambs	62	G11
Sawtry Cambs	61	Q4
Saxby Leics	73	L7
Saxby Lincs	86	D3
Saxby All Saints N Linc	92	G7
Saxelbye Leics	72	H6
Saxham Street Suffk	64	F9
Saxilby Lincs	85	Q5
Saxlingham Norfk	76	E4
Saxlingham Green Norfk	65	J2
Saxlingham Nethergate Norfk	65	J2
Saxlingham Thorpe Norfk	65	J2
Saxmundham Suffk	65	M9
Saxondale Notts	72	H3
Saxon Street Cambs	63	L9
Saxtead Suffk	65	K8
Saxtead Green Suffk	65	K9
Saxtead Little Green Suffk	65	J8
Saxthorpe Norfk	76	G5
Saxton N York	91	M3
Sayers Common W Susx	24	G7
Scackleton N York	98	C6
Scadabay W Isls	168	g8
Scadabhagh W Isls	168	g8
Scafell Pike Cumb	100	H9
Scaftworth Notts	85	M3
Scagglethorpe N York	98	G6
Scalasaig Ag & B	136	b3
Scalby E R Yk	92	D3
Scalby N York	99	L2
Scald End Bed	61	M9
Scaldwell Nhants	60	G6
Scaleby Cumb	110	H8